D1094251

4

REALM of
NUMBERS

By the same author

Fiction

Pebble in the Sky
I, Robot
The Stars Like Dust
Foundation
Foundation and Empire
The Currents of Space
Second Foundation
The Caves of Steel
The Martian Way and Other Stories
The End of Eternity
The Naked Sun
Earth is Room Enough
The Death Dealers
Nine Tomorrows

Non-Fiction

Biochemistry and Human Metabolism*
The Chemicals of Life
Races and People*
Chemistry and Human Health*
Inside the Atom
Building Blocks of the Universe
Only a Trillion
The World of Carbon
The World of Nitrogen
Words of Science
Realm of Numbers

in collaboration

4

R E A L M *of*

N U M B E R S

Isaac Asimov

diagrams by Robert Belmore

HOUGHTON MIFFLIN COMPANY BOSTON

The Riverside Press Cambridge

C O N T E N T S

1	Digits and — Digits	1
2	Nothing — and Less than Nothing	18
3	By-Passing Addition	35
4	Broken Numbers	57
5	Breakage by Tens	73
6	The Shape of Numbers	98
7	Digging for Roots	114
8	The Very Large and Very Small	133
9	From Number Line to Number Area	165
10	Endlessness	183

1

1

1
Digits and — Digits
1

NAMING NUMBERS

THE NUMBER SENSE is not confined to the human race. Various animals can be trained to distinguish between different numbers of objects. Naturally, no one imagines they consciously count objects, but they can apparently tell the difference between numbers by the differences in the patterns formed by different numbers.

Most of us, for instance, still go by pattern in dealing with playing cards after even a short acquaintance. To be sure, each card has a small number in the upper left-hand corner, but the average cardplayer doesn't really need that. The accompanying sketches of playing cards are without numbers. Does that bother you? Or do you recognize the cards at a glance anyway, and without counting?

The crucial point in man's mathematical history came when more than patterns were required; when more was needed than a look inside the cave to assure himself that both children were present,

PLAYING CARDS WITHOUT NUMBERS

or a glance at his rack of stone axes to convince himself that all four spares were in place.

At some point, man found it necessary to communicate numbers. He had to go to a neighbor and say, "Listen, old man, you didn't lift one of my stone axes last time you were in my cave, did you?" Then, if the neighbor were to say, "Good heavens, what makes you think that?" it would be convenient to be able to say, "You see, friend, I had four spares before you came to visit and only three after you left."

In short, it is useful to have names for different numbers.

Undoubtedly only a few names were invented at first, just enough to get by on. Some primitive tribes even today don't have names for any number higher than two or three. (This doesn't mean they don't know about higher numbers, of course. It just means they don't have separate names for them. They might call the number we call four, "three and one more.")

In almost all cases, though, separate names were given to the first ten numbers. These names, in English, are: one, two, three, four, five, six, seven, eight, nine, and ten.

One could go on to invent names for numbers over ten without limit, but this would become unwieldy. How would one remember which sound meant "forty-three" and which "seventy-nine" and so on? Through ten, on the other hand, things were easy because one had a built-in memory system handy until the ten number-names were well fixed in mind.

When you said "four," you held up four fingers; for "six" you held up six fingers. Then, if your listener observed your fingers, he could see what you meant just in case he forgot exactly how much was represented by the sounds "four" and "six."

The Latin word for "finger" is "digitus" and, in English, fingers are sometimes called "digits." It is no accident that the first ten numbers are also called digits. In the beginning, fingers and numbers were practically identical.

It may seem to you that we do have names for numbers over ten; but that's just appearance. The changes in language have so distorted number names that we have forgotten the original meanings.

The word "eleven" is not really a separate name but comes from primitive Teutonic words meaning "one left over."

In other words, we can imagine our man holding up all ten fingers and saying, "And one left over."

Similarly, "twelve" meant "two left over" to begin with.

From there on, things are clearer. "Thirteen" is obviously a slurring of "three and ten"; "fourteen" is even closer to "four and ten," and so on through the teens. By the time you get to "twenty," you have a corruption of "two tens," so that "twenty-three" means "two tens and three." "Thirty," "forty," "fifty," and the rest work out similarly, and that carries us through to "ninety-nine."

FINGER CODES

But have we lost the aid of our fingers once we pass ten? How would you indicate, to take an example, a number like fifty-four on your fingers? I have seen youngsters open their hands rapidly five times in succession, indicating five tens or fifty, then hold up four fingers. This is fine except that the watcher has to be on the alert, counting the number of times that the hands open. Usually, he has to play it safe and ask, at the end, "Fifty-four?" which makes the whole finger display useless.

Of course, we never develop finger techniques properly for numbers over ten because we learn other and better tricks at school. If we didn't, we might develop a device something like this: We could agree that when we hold hands palms inward, the number of fingers held up would indicate the number of tens. Then, when hands are held palms outward, the number of fingers would indicate the number of ones.

You could indicate fifty-four then, by holding up five fingers palms-in and four fingers palms-out. In this way, two gestures would give any number up to ninety-nine.

The number beyond ninety-nine is "ten tens" and this could be shown by ten fingers palms-in, but then what can be done for "eleven tens"?

Well, when we reached "ten," we started a new system of counting by "tens," instead of "ones." Now that we've reached "ten tens," we can start still another series and count by "ten tens." Our word for "ten tens" is "hundred," an old word whose origin is lost in antiquity.

Thus, after reaching a hundred, we can start all over. One more than a hundred is "a hundred and one" (what could be clearer?). We work our way onward through "a hundred and twenty-three," "a hundred and seventy-nine," all the way up to "a hundred and ninety-nine," followed, of course, by "two hundred." In this way we can proceed up to "nine hundred and ninety-nine" and the number after that is "ten hundred."

By this time, we're in the habit of inventing new names for any number that reaches the "ten" point. In the case of "ten hundred," the new word is "thousand," another word of primeval origin.

By sticking to this principle of new names for every ten of something, we can continue to use our fingers. We can, for instance, agree that fingers pointing downward palms-in mean "thousands" while fingers pointing downward palms-out mean "hundreds."

Therefore, if we want to indicate seven thousand five hundred and twenty-four by fingers, we can do it in four motions: seven fingers down palms-in, then five fingers down palms-out, then two fingers up palms-in, then four fingers up palms-out.

Under primitive conditions, it is practically never necessary to go higher than the thousands and our number system shows that. When ten thousand is reached, there is no new name for it. It's just "ten

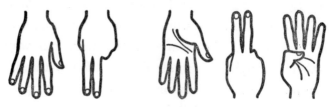

FINGERS INDICATING 7524

thousand" and after that "eleven thousand," "twenty-three thousand," and so on.

The Greek mathematicians did work up a special name for ten thousand. They called it "myrias" (from which comes our word "myriad") but that was only used by a small specialized group, and never reached the common man. Nowadays we have names for numbers like "million" and "billion" but these weren't invented till the late Middle Ages.

For most of man's history, then, four finger-gestures would have been enough for almost everything.

PEBBLE CODES

This is not to say that my system of finger gestures was ever actually used. By the time it became necessary to work with numbers in the hundreds and thousands, someone had invented a box of artificial fingers, which we call by the (originally Greek) name of "abacus."

The abacus, in its simplest form, consists of a wooden frame across which run a number of wires. On each wire are strung ten disks. (The disks of the Greek and Roman versions were, originally, rounded pebbles placed in grooves, rather than on wires. The Latin word for "pebble" is "calculus" and mankind has been using such pebbles as representing numbers for so long that we still say we are "calculating" when we are manipulating numbers. And the disks themselves — even similar disks used for other purposes — are called "counters.")

Each wire with its ten counters represents a pair of hands with ten fingers. There is a short stretch of clear space on each wire so that if you start with all the counters at the left, moving one or more to the right is the equivalent of raising one or more fingers.

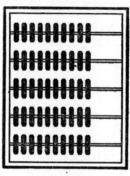

1   ABACUS

Suppose the bottom wire, or rung, represents "ones," the one above it "tens," the one above "hundreds," and the one above that "thousands." Now, to represent seven thousand five hundred and twenty-four, it is only necessary to move four counters to the right on the bottom rung, two to the right on the rung above it, five to the right on the next higher rung and seven to the right on the rung above that.

This has several advantages over the finger code. In the first place, you don't have to remember whether fingers go up or down or palms go in or out. That cuts out one strain on the memory. Secondly, in finger code, you have to show one number after another. Your watcher must remember the seven thousands while you go on to the five hundreds and so on. In the abacus, all the categories remain in view simultaneously and can stay in view

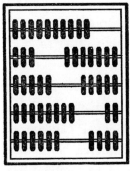

2 ABACUS INDICATING 7524

indefinitely. Another strain on the memory is removed.

Thirdly, by adding rungs to the abacus, you can carry numbers as high as you please with no additional trouble. Finally, the abacus makes it possible to combine two numbers easily and get the quantity represented by both together.

MANEUVERING THE PEBBLES

The necessity for combining or "adding" numbers

must have arisen quite early in human history. If you stole the next man's supply of stone axes, for instance (or acquired them honestly, for that matter), or if your ewes gave birth to a certain number of lambs, you would want to know how many stone axes or sheep you had altogether.

The simplest way is to count. You had five; two more are added; you count the lot and find you have seven. After a while, through long experience, you don't have to count five and two. You know in advance it's going to come out seven.

Of course, though, there's a limit to how far memory will serve. If it is necessary to add twenty-three and fifty-four, you may well not know in advance what the answer will be. And to count numbers at that level can be tedious and even infuriating. A primitive herdsman trying to count twenty-three sheep to which fifty-four more have been added, and having just succeeded in losing count for the second time, may be an enraged herdsman indeed, whom it would be a good idea to stay away from.

The abacus supplies one solution to this problem since it is a mechanical device that will do your adding for you with a minimum exercise of your own intellect. You won't even need to stay near those infuriating sheep, but can go indoors.

If you wish to add twenty-three and fifty-four

on the abacus, set up twenty-three first by moving three counters on the "ones" rung and two on the "tens" rung. Then add the fifty-four by pushing out four more counters on the "ones" rung and five more on the "tens" rung. Now if you count all the counters you have moved, you find seven counters in the "ones" and seven in the "tens." Twenty-three and fifty-four are seventy-seven and you have not had to count higher than ten at any stage in the process.

In fact, had you wished, you could have added much higher numbers without any more trouble. For instance, two hundred fifty-three thousand one hundred and twelve plus one hundred twenty-six thousand eight hundred and thirty-one would, by abacus, quickly come out as three hundred seventy-nine thousand nine hundred and forty-three. *Still*, you would not have had to count above ten at any stage of the addition.

But suppose you had occasion to add eight and seven. Strangely enough, this presents a greater problem than the addition in the hundreds of thousands which I just mentioned. This time, you see, you run out of counters. You begin by shoving eight counters to the right. Your next desire would be to move seven more counters to the right, but having moved eight already, there are only two left to move. What to do?

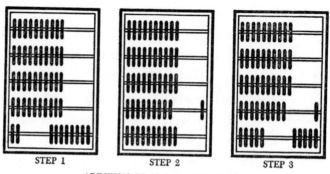

STEP 1   STEP 2   STEP 3

ADDITION OF 8 AND 7 ON ABACUS

Yet the answer is simple. You move those two and now have all ten counters of the "ones" rung at the right. You can exchange them, so to speak, for one counter in the "tens" rung, since ten "ones" is one "ten." Move your ten counters in the "ones" row back to the left, then, and in their place move one counter to the right in the "tens" row.

Now complete your move in the "ones" row. You were going to move seven counters but were only able to move two. That still leaves you five counters to move, so move them. Read the final result: one counter to the right in the "tens" row, five in the "ones" row; eight plus seven is fifteen.

This sort of trading ten for one works all the way up the rungs. If you need more than ten tens, you can always exchange ten tens for one hundred; you can exchange ten hundreds for one thousand and so on.

Through it all, it is still never necessary to count more than ten counters at any one time. Actually, it is never necessary to count higher than five, since, if you have pushed more than five to the right, you need only count the number still on the left (always less than five) to know how many are on the right. If there is only one counter on the left, you know there are nine on the right.

Five counters or less can be told at a glance by the pattern, without the necessity of actual counting. For this reason, despite the necessity of continually swapping ten for one, a skilled abacus operator can perform complicated additions and subtractions (the latter by working in reverse) with a speed far quicker than can be managed by most of us with pencil and paper in the ordinary fashion. A champion abacus operator can even hold his own surprisingly well against electric desk computers.

Incidentally, by working the abacus you can show that it doesn't matter with which number of a sum you start. Whether you move seven counters first, then eight, or eight first, then seven, you end up with fifteen. Remember as a general rule, then, that it doesn't matter in what order a group of numbers are added.

LETTER CODES

The abacus was fine in its way, but it still leaves

one problem. How does one write down numbers for permanent records? The ancient Babylonians and Egyptians had plenty of occasion to write down large numbers in figuring out taxes and tributes or in listing supplies bought for the king's household.

One could, of course, write numbers just like any other word and say (as I have said earlier in the chapter) two hundred fifty-three thousand one hundred and twelve, or the equivalent in Babylonian or Egyptian. This, however, can be very tedious. Some sort of shorthand would be very desirable.

And some sort of shorthand was always adopted. Scribes used various signs and symbols (often simply letters of the alphabet) to indicate numbers. For an example, let's consider the Roman system, because this is still used on monuments and public buildings, on diplomas and clockfaces, so that it is familiar to all of us.

To indicate one, the Romans wrote I, which probably indicated one finger. Two, three, and four were II, III, and IIII, which is simple enough. For five, the symbol is V. No one knows why, but the favorite suggestion is that it represents an upraised palm with the thumb held away from the other fingers. Following this are VI, VII, VIII and VIIII. Ten is represented by X (possibly two palms, one up and one down). Further, fifty is L, hundred is C, five hundred is D, and thousand is M.

To write one thousand nine hundred and fifty-eight, one would write MDCCCCLVIII (one thousand plus five hundred plus one hundred plus one hundred plus one hundred plus one hundred plus fifty plus five plus one plus one plus one).

Notice that in the Roman system, a particular symbol always had the same number value no matter where in the number it was. If instead of writing MDCCCCLVIII, I had written CLCDIIVCMCI, it would still be the same number. The only reason for arranging it in order of decreasing symbols is so that the scribe could add up the symbols quickly and get the meaning. (It's like picking up a bridge hand. The hand has the same value however the cards are arranged, but you arrange them in suits and according to decreasing value just for convenience.)*

The fact that Roman numbers have no place-value destroys the system that works so well on the abacus. In the abacus, you see, it is important to know on which rung the counters are moved, since each rung has its own value.

---

* Nowadays it is customary to put a smaller symbol before a larger one as a sign that it ought to be sub-tracted, so that IV rather than IIII is "four," and CM rather than DCCCC is "nine hundred." However, this was a space-saving medieval development, and was not used by the earlier Romans.

To be sure, you could still add, using Roman numerals. For instance, if you wanted to add one thousand nine hundred and fifty-eight and two thousand four hundred seventy-two, you could write MDCCCCLVIII and MMCCCCLXXII for the two numbers, then write a new number incorporating all the symbols: MMMDCCCCCCCCCLLXXVIIIII.

Now to simplify that: five I's are a V, and two L's are a C, so you can write:

MMMDCCCCCCCCCXXVV.

But two V's are an X, and five C's are a D, so now the number is: MMMDDCCCCXXX. However, two D's are an M, so we make a last change to MMMMCCCCXXX and have our answer: four thousand four hundred thirty.

No doubt the skilled Roman scribe could do this addition very quickly, being used to it. But there are other types of number manipulations that are bone-crackers using the Roman system but simple on the abacus.

As a matter of fact, the lack of a proper system of writing numbers held back the advance of Greek mathematics, since the Greek system was no more sensible than the Roman system. It is said that if the greatest of the Greek mathematicians, Archimedes, had only had our number system, he would have invented calculus (which he nearly invented anyway), and it would not have had to wait eighteen hundred years for Newton to invent it.

It wasn't until the ninth century A.D. that some unnamed Hindu first thought up the modern system. This discovery reached the Arabs, by whom it was transmitted to the Europeans, so that we call modern numbers "Arabic numerals." The discovery in India was simply that of modeling numbers on the abacus (as I will soon explain). Since the abacus works so well, it's a wonder the discovery hung fire as long as it did.

2
2
2
Nothing — and Less than Nothing
2

THE HINDUS began with nine different symbols, one for each of the numbers from one through nine. These have changed through history but reached their present form in Europe in the sixteenth century and are now written: 1, 2, 3, 4, 5, 6, 7, 8, and 9.

This in itself was not unique. The Greeks and Hebrews, for instance, used nine different symbols for these numbers. In each case, the symbols were the first nine letters of their alphabets. The Greeks and Hebrews went on, though, to use the next nine letters of their alphabets for ten, twenty, thirty, and so on; and the nine letters after that for one hundred, two hundred, three hundred, and so on. If the alphabet wasn't long enough for the purpose (twenty-eight letters are required to reach a thousand by this system) archaic letters or special forms of letters were added.

The use of letters for numbers gave rise to confusion with words. For instance, the Hebrew number "fifteen" made use of the two letters that began the name of God (in the Hebrew language) and so some other letter combination had to be used.

On the other hand, ordinary words could be converted into numbers by adding up the numerical value of the letters composing it. This was done especially for words and names in the Bible (a process called "gematria") and all sorts of mystical and occult meanings were read into it. The most familiar example is the passage in the Revelation of St. John where the number of the "beast" is given as six hundred and sixty-six. This undoubtedly meant that some contemporary figure, whom it was unsafe to name openly (probably the Roman Emperor Nero) had a name which, in Hebrew or Greek letters, added up to that figure. Ever since then, however, people have been trying to fit the names of their enemies into that sum.

Where the Hindus improved on the Greek and Hebrew system, however, was in using the same nine figures for tens, hundreds, and indeed for any rung of the abacus. Out of those nine figures, they built up all numbers. All that was necessary was to give the figures positional values.

For instance, the number twenty-three, on the abacus, consisted of three counters moved to the right on the "ones" rung and two on the "tens" rung. The number can therefore be written 23, the

numeral on the right representing the bottom rung
on the abacus and the one on the left the next
higher one.

Obviously, thirty-two would then be written 32
and the positional values become plain since 23
and 32 are not the same number. One is two tens
plus three ones and the other three tens plus
two ones.

It is very unlikely that the clever Greeks did not
think of this; they thought of many much more
subtle points. What must have stopped them (and
everyone else until the day of the unknown Hindu
genius) was the dilemma of the untouched rung on
the abacus.

Suppose you wanted, instead of twenty-three, to
write two hundred and three. On the abacus, you
would move two counters on the "hundreds" rung
and two on the "ones" rung. The "tens" rung would
remain untouched. Using the Hindu system, it
might seem you would still have to write 23, only
this time the 2 means "two hundreds," not "two
tens."

For that matter, how would you write two thousand and three, or two thousand and thirty, or two
thousand three hundred? In each case, you would
have to move two counters on one rung and three on
another. They would all seem to be 23.

One solution might be to use different symbols for

each rung, but that was what the Greeks did and
that was unsatisfactory. Or you might use some
sort of symbol above each figure to indicate the
rung. You might write twenty-three as $\overset{..}{23}$ and
two hundred and three as $\overset{.\,.}{23}$, indicating that in
the second case, the 2 was in the third or "hundreds"
rung, rather than in the second or "tens" rung.
This would make the numbers rather difficult to
read in a hurry, though the system would work
in theory.

No, the great Hindu innovation was the *invention*
of a special symbol for an untouched abacus row.
This symbol the Arabs called "sifr," meaning
"empty," since the space at the right end of an
untouched abacus rung was empty. This word has
come down to us as "cipher" or, in more corrupt
form, as "zero."

Our symbol for zero is 0, and so we write twenty-
three as 23, two hundred and three as 203, two
thousand and three as 2003, two hundred and
thirty as 230, two thousand and thirty as 2030,
two thousand three hundred as 2300, and so on.
In each case, we show the untouched rungs on the
abacus by using zeros.

(Twenty-three could be written as 0023 or
0000000023, depending on the size of the abacus,
but this is never done. It is always assumed that

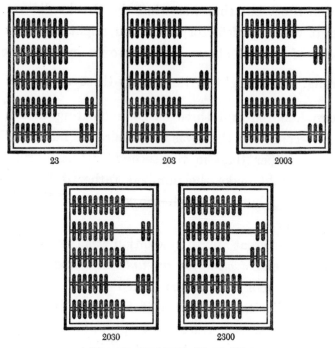

NUMBERS WITH ZERO ON ABACUS

all rungs of the abacus above the first one mentioned and all numerals to the left of the first one mentioned are zero.)

It was the zero that made our so-called Arabic numerals practical and revolutionized the use of numbers. (Strange that the discovery of "nothing" could be so world-shakingly important; and stranger still that so many great mathematicians never saw that "nothing.")

Such is the importance of zero that, to this day,

one word for the manipulation of numbers is "ciphering" and when we work out a problem (even one not involving numbers), we "decipher" it. The awe in which the numerals were held by people who didn't understand their working is recalled to us by the fact that any secret writing, usually called a "cryptogram," may also be called a "cipher."

MOVING THE COUNTERS ON PAPER

In adding by Arabic numerals, it is first necessary to memorize the sums obtained by combining any two of the numerals from 0 to 9. In the first grade, children laboriously memorize that 2 and 3 make 5; 4 and 5 make 9; 6 and 7 make 13, and so on. Also, most important of all, 0 and 0 make 0.

On an abacus such sums can be performed without having to memorize as much as the sum of 1 and 1, only the knowledge of counting to 10 being necessary. Certainly the advantage of written numerals over the abacus seems well hidden at this stage.

But suppose you were required to add large numbers — 5894 and 2578, for instance. Knowing the small sums is all that is necessary. First, break up each number into thousands, hundreds, tens, and ones, so that the problem looks like this:

	5000	and	800	and	90	and	4
plus	2000	and	500	and	70	and	8
makes	7000	and	1300	and	160	and	12

Now if the number 1300 is broken up into 1000 and 300, 160 is broken up into 100 and 60, and 12 is broken up into 10 and 2, it is a simple matter to add up the thousands, hundreds, tens and ones to come out with:

        8000   and   400   and   70   and   2

or 8472.

The way you are actually taught to add numbers makes use of this principle but simplifies it by omitting zeros and "carrying" ones so that the problem looks like this:

$$\begin{array}{r} 5894 \\ 2578 \\ \hline 8472 \end{array}$$

Either way, what you have done, automatically and without the necessity of deep thought, is to make ten-for-one swaps. You pushed ten ones into the tens column, ten tens into the hundreds column and ten hundreds into the thousands column.

Subtracting is the reverse process. If, for instance, we are subtracting 298 from 531, we break up the numbers as follows:

                500   and   30   and   1

    minus   200   and   90   and   8

At first glance, it looks as though there will be trouble subtracting 8 from 1 or 90 from 30, so we rewrite the top number, borrowing 100 from the 500, adding it to the 30 to make it 130; then borrow-

ing 10 from the 130 to add to the 1. Now the
problem looks like this:

	400	and	120	and	11
minus	200	and	90	and	8
	200	and	30	and	3

so the answer is 233.

Our usual method of subtraction does not look
like this, because we are taught a mechanical
method that obscures the principle; nevertheless
the principle is there.

A skilled abacus worker could solve the problems
just mentioned, using counters instead of numerals,
and get the answer far faster than would the average
worker with numerals. However, the abacus takes
manual skill and numerals don't.

Moreover, in numerical computation, all your
steps are in plain view so that they can be checked
for error, whereas on the abacus, if your finger slips
at some point, you cannot ever know where or why
you made the error. What's more, just as the
abacus is more permanent than finger gestures, so
are numbers on paper more permanent than the
abacus.

BREAKING THE ZERO BARRIER

A beginner in arithmetic quickly learns that any
two numbers may be added with a reasonable
answer resulting. He also quickly learns that this is
not true of subtraction.

If you take 5 from 7, you have 2 left. If you take 7 from 7, you have 0 left. But can you take eight from seven?

The Greeks decided "No!" with a large exclamation point. Subtracting 8 from 7 would leave less than nothing and how can anything be less than nothing, since nothing is the least possible?

This reasoning was followed until the 1500's. And yet, if we stop to think of it, it is very easy for something to be less than nothing.

Suppose, for instance, that you had $7 and a friend came up and reminded you that you owed him $8. Being honest, you promptly give him the $7, explain that this is all you have and promise to pay the final $1 as soon as you get hold of the sum.

Now you are left with less than no money, since you are $1 in debt. In other words, take 8 from 7 and you have "one less than zero." What's odd or hard to believe about that?

Or suppose you plan to walk to the next town which happens to be 7 miles to the south. You begin then at a point 7 miles north of the town. Walk 1 mile and you are 6 miles north; walk 2 miles and you are 5 miles north. This continues until you have walked 7 miles, at which point you are 0 miles north of the town; you are there.

But suppose you are extremely absent-minded

(or extremely stubborn) and walk 8 miles. That puts you 1 mile on the other side of town; 1 mile *south* of the town. Now as we walked 7 miles, our distance to the town decreased to zero. If we walk more than 7 miles shouldn't it continue decreasing below zero?

You might say, "No. It starts increasing again."

But the increasing distance is now south of the town, where it was north previously. Doesn't that make a difference?

To see if it makes a useful difference, let's draw a vertical line (which would be north–south on the usual map). Let's next place a dot upon it, representing a town (or anything else), and call that dot zero. Now, if we mark off even divisions above that mark (that is, to the north, according to our map conventions) we can pretend they are mile intervals and number them 1, 2, 3, and so on. We can do the same for equal intervals below the dot (to the south) and label those 1, 2, 3, and so on, also. The ones above we can call ordinary numbers and the ones below we can call "less-than-zero" numbers.

We'll need some symbol to differentiate between these two sets of numbers. The system actually used involves the process by which the numbers are obtained. Ordinary numbers are the only ones that are obtained when two ordinary numbers are

added. The symbol for addition is the "plus" sign
(+). Ordinary numbers are therefore written +1,

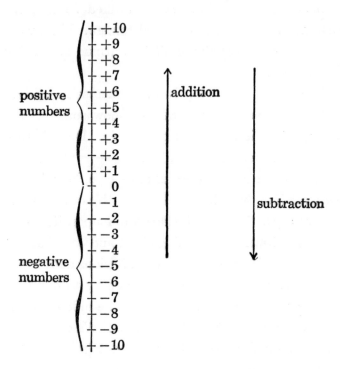

+2, +3, and so on. These are called positive
numbers, the word "positive" giving the impression
that they "positively exist." They are the "real
thing."

Numbers less than zero are obtained by subtracting as, for instance, taking 3 from 2, which
leaves a less-than-zero number. Subtraction is
indicated by the "minus" sign (−), so the less-

than-zero numbers are written: -1, -2, -3, and so on.*

These less-than-zero numbers are more properly called negative numbers, the word "negative" coming from a Latin word meaning "to deny." Even when mathematicians were finally forced to use negative numbers, they apparently had to indicate some sort of denial that they "really" existed.

Now that we have our vertical line marked off (and notice that 0 is neither positive nor negative), we can do addition and subtraction upon it. Since positive numbers increase upward and addition increases numbers, let's say that addition means moving up the scale. Since subtraction is the reverse of addition, it must imply moving down the scale.

Suppose, then, we want to add $+2$ and $+5$. This can be written as $(+2) + (+5)$, the parentheses being used to indicate that the $+$ sign within them belongs to the numeral and is not a sign of addition.

---

* Our plus and minus signs date back to the 1500's. The plus sign probably arose from the habit of writing a sum such as "two and three" with the use of the ampersand for the sake of quickness. The ampersand (&) appears in the written form as &, and 2 & 3 quickly becomes $2 + 3$. The origin of the minus sign is a matter of argument. There are a number of theories but none sounds particularly good.

So accustomed are we, however, to positive numbers as just numbers, that it is customary to leave out the plus sign unless there is some special reason for calling attention to their positiveness. So the sum is written simply, $2 + 5$.

On our number scale, this means we must start at the point $+2$ and move up (because we're adding) 5 intervals. This brings us to the $+7$ point, so $2 + 5 = 7$. (Notice that if you had started at $+5$ and gone up 2 intervals, you would still have ended at $+7$. Again I point out that as a general rule it doesn't matter in which order you add numbers: $2 + 5 = 5 + 2$.)

Now suppose you wanted to subtract $+2$ from $+5$, a state of affairs which can be written $(+5) - (+2)$ or, more simply, $5 - 2$. This time, we start at the $+5$ point and move down (because we're subtracting) 2 intervals. This brings us to the $+3$ point, so $5 - 2 = 3$.

The important point, now, is to discover whether negative numbers can be handled by the same techniques used for positive numbers. If they can, then regardless of their "meaning," they would be just as useful as positive numbers. This would be of more than theoretical interest. Negative numbers are not only enormously useful in science and engineering, but have practical applications in everyday affairs, too. For instance, in bookkeeping assets are handled as positive numbers and debits as negative numbers.

HANDLING THE NEGATIVES

To begin with, suppose you wanted to subtract 5 from 2; that is, to solve the problem, $2 - 5$. Using the same system as before, we start at the $+2$ point and move down 5 intervals. This carries us through the zero point and down to the -3 point; consequently $2 - 5 = -3$. This seems straightforward enough, and it shows us one important thing: $5 - 2$ is *not* equal to $2 - 5$. In subtraction (unlike addition), it *does* matter in which order the numbers are taken.

But what if we start at the negative end of the scale? Suppose we want to add -2 and $+5$. (From here to the end of the chapter, let's keep parentheses so that we don't confuse negative numbers with subtraction and positive numbers with addition. The problem just stated is therefore written $(-2) + (+5)$.) To do this, using the usual system, begin at the -2 point and move up 5 intervals. We end at the $+3$ point; so $(-2) + (+5) = +3$.

Does this make sense? Well, if you are $2 in debt and earn $5, this puts you $3 in the black; you are left with $3 after paying off your debt.

We can also move downward on the negative end of the scale. Take $+5$ from -2, for instance; that is, solve the problem of $(-2) - (+5)$. Begin at the -2 point and move down (since we are subtracting) 5 intervals, which brings us to the -7 point; thus $(-2) - (+5) = -7$. Or, in the same practical terms as before, if you begin with a $2 debt and are forced to borrow an additional $5, so that you incur an additional $5 debt, you end by being $7 in debt altogether.

And still negative numbers are behaving just as normally and decently and sensibly as positive numbers.

There is still one maneuver we haven't tried. So far, we have been adding and subtracting only positive numbers. What if we try to add or subtract a negative number?

In practical terms, this means we are going to be adding or subtracting debts. Now if I were to take a $5 debt away from you, you can see that it is the same as giving you $5. If, on the other hand, I give you a $5 debt (and force you to accept it somehow), you are $5 poorer; I might just as well have taken $5 in cash out of your pocket.

What this means in arithmetical terms is that subtracting -5 is the same as adding $+5$, and that adding -5 is the same as subtracting $+5$.

This gives us the opportunity to wipe out subtraction altogether, since any problem of the shape of $5 - 2$ is really $(+5) - (+2)$ and can be written,

according to the rule just stated, as $(+5) + (-2)$.
Both versions give the same answer. In both cases
we start at the $+5$ point and move down 2 intervals.
In the case of $(+5) - (+2)$, this is obvious; subtraction means "move down."

In the case of $(+5) + (-2)$, it is less obvious.
The plus sign between the numbers is addition and
means "go up." But you're adding a negative
number, which reverses things so that the two facts
together mean "go up in reverse"; and to "go up in
reverse" is to "go down." So in either case, the
answer is $+3$.

But why should anyone want to change a subtraction into an addition, when it just means becoming devious and having to say "go up in reverse"
instead of the simple, direct "go down"? Ah, but
addition has this advantage, generally, over subtraction: the order of the numbers does not matter
in addition; it does in subtraction.

The expression $(+5) - (+2)$ is not the same as
$(+2) - (+5)$, as I have already pointed out. The
answer to the first is $+3$ and to the latter, -3. On
the other hand, the equivalent expression $(+5) +$
(-2) is the same as $(-2) + (+5)$. In both cases,
the answer is $+3$. Obviously, then, by switching
to addition whenever possible, we remove the chance
of one type of error, that of placing numbers in the
wrong order by accident.

The situation is similar in subtracting a negative number. The problem $(+5) - (-2)$ can be written, if we choose, $(+5) + (+2)$. In the first case, we start at the $+5$ point of the scale and "go down in reverse" 2 intervals. To "go down in reverse" is to "go up" and going up 2 intervals brings us to $+7$. And, of course, this is exactly what happens if we solve $(+5) + (+2)$.

This business of eliminating subtraction and working with addition only is usually first encountered by students when they begin to study algebra. For that reason, adding negative numbers (instead of subtracting positive ones) is often called algebraic addition. Actually, though, there's no reason for such a name. It's perfectly straightforward arithmetic and algebra has nothing to do with it.

By-Passing Addition

PLUS AND PLUS AND PLUS AND PLUS

SUPPOSE YOU DREW A SQUARE which was 1 inch long on each side. You could call it a "square inch" and use it as a unit of area.

Consider next a second square, which is 2 inches long on each side. If you divide this 2-inch square in half lengthwise and in half widthwise, you end with 4 smaller squares, each one of which is a 1-inch square. Another square that is 3 inches long and 3 inches wide can be cut up into square-inch sections by dividing it into 3 equal parts both lengthwise and widthwise. The result is 9 square inches within our 3-inch square.

Finally, a similar treatment of an oblong 6 inches wide and 9 inches long breaks it up into 54 square inches. All of this is shown in the accompanying figures.

In each of these cases, the square-inch portions are arranged in ranks (which are horizontal rows) and files (which are vertical rows). Each file contains as many square inches as the square or oblong is long (in inches) and there are as many files altogether as the square or oblong is wide (in inches).

In the 2-inch square, there are 2 square-inch sections in each of 2 files and $2 + 2 = 4$. In the 3-inch square, there are 3 square-inch sections in each of 3 files, and $3 + 3 + 3 = 9$. Finally, in the 6-inch by 9-inch oblong, there are 9 square-inch sections in each of 6 files, or (if you look at it sideways) 6 square-inch sections in each of 9 files. In the first case, the number of square inches is $9 + 9 + 9 + 9 + 9 + 9$, and in the second case it is $6 + 6 + 6 + 6 + 6 + 6 + 6 + 6 + 6$. It

1	2	3	4	5	6	
1	2	3	4	5	6	1
7	8	9	10	11	12	2
13	14	15	16	17	18	3
19	20	21	22	23	24	4
25	26	27	28	29	30	5
31	32	33	34	35	36	6
37	38	39	40	41	42	7
43	44	45	46	47	48	8
49	50	51	52	53	54	9

AREAS

doesn't matter which case you choose, because both add up to 54.

In general, obtaining areas of figures involves this kind of repeated addition. In squares and oblongs, the matter is fairly simple. It gets a bit more complicated in triangles and circles and still more complicated in areas of irregular shape. Yet this sort of thing had to be done continuously even in early agricultural civilizations (let alone our own highly technological one). Farms had to be surveyed and areas calculated even if only to adjust the tax rate. (Sometimes I think it was taxes more than anything else that encouraged the development of arithmetic.)

However, just as the necessity of repeated counting forced the development of a system of addition, so the necessity of repeated additions forced the development of a new type of number manipulation.

To begin with, let's adopt a new notation and write 6×9 ("six times nine," with $\times$ being the "multiplication sign") when we mean nine 6's added together or six 9's. As I have shown in this particular case (and as you can check for yourself in other cases), it doesn't matter which it is; $6 \times 9 = 9 \times 6$.

We can use this new notation by stating as a general rule the fact that the area of any square or oblong is equal to its length times its width, and the next step is to find some simple way of handling multiplication. Of course, repeated addition as in 6×9 is always open to us, but this could become complicated.

If we were interested in the area of an oblong lot that was 129 feet long and 54 feet wide, we would have to multiply 129 by 54 to get the answer (in square feet, of course, not square inches). This would mean adding up a hundred twenty-nine 54's or fifty-four 129's. In either case, it would be a wearisome job.

Or, if in some commercial transaction, 254 dozen

objects were bought at 72¢ a dozen, the total payment (in cents) would be 254×72. Now it would be necessary to add up two hundred and fifty-four 72's or seventy-two 254's. This sort of problem comes up constantly even in ordinary life and it would pay to devise some short cut that would not involve repeated addition.

EACH BY EACH

Again the secret lies in memorization. It is necessary to memorize the "multiplication table," consisting of all the possible combinations of two digits up to and including 9×9. The school child has to recite $5 \times 2 = 10$ and $8 \times 7 = 56$ until it seems to be coming out of his ears. However, once he grinds this in deeply enough, he'll find it will be all he'll need to multiply any two numbers, however large.

One thing that is particularly important to remember is that multiplication by zero gives an answer that is always zero. Thus $5 \times 0 = 0$; $155 \times 0 = 0$; $148273695 \times 0 = 0$; and, of course, $0 \times 0 = 0$. You can look at all these examples as representing the addition of 5 zeros or 155 zeros and so on. Naturally, it doesn't matter how many zeros you add together; the result is always zero.

This means that having learned that $3 \times 7 = 21$, it follows that $30 \times 7 = 210$ and $3 \times 70 = 210$.

The zero in neither case is affected by multiplication. If you multiply 30 × 70, the result is 2100, both zeros persisting unaffected by the process.

Next, if you want to multiply a number containing several digits other than zeros, it is only necessary to break it up in the usual way. For instance, what is the product of 3965 × 7? (The result of a multiplication is called a "product," just as the result of an addition is called a "sum.") Positional notation allows us to break up 3965 into 3000 and 900 and 60 and 5. This gives us numbers consisting only of a single digit and various numbers of zeros, so nothing more than our multiplication table is needed. Each number is multiplied in turn by 7, the partial products are added and the complete product obtained, as follows:

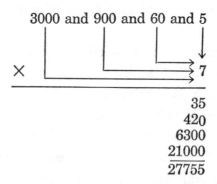

$$
\begin{array}{r}
35 \\
420 \\
6300 \\
21000 \\
\hline
27755 \\
\end{array}
$$

It doesn't matter in which order we perform the multiplications, left to right, right to left, or skipping around. I did it right to left because that is the way it is usually taught in the elementary grades. Furthermore we are taught to leave the number unbroken and to ignore zeros so that the problem looks like this when solved:

$$
\begin{array}{r}
3965 \\
\times\ 7 \\
\hline
35 \\
42 \\
63 \\
21 \\
\hline
27755
\end{array}
$$

We are even taught to carry some of the numbers mentally so that we can dispense with the partial products on occasion. All this is just a matter of mechanics which does not affect the principle of multiplication. The advantage of the mechanics is that the youngster learns to multiply speedily, and with a minimum of thought. The disadvantage is that he sometimes never finds out why he does what he has been taught to do; why he indents the partial products, for instance.

Where both numbers in a multiplication problem are higher than 10, there is a slight additional complication. Both numbers can be broken up and then each of the number parts above is multiplied by each of the number parts below and the partial products are again added. Thus 35 × 28 breaks up as follows (and it is the presence of the crossed lines indicating the manner of multiplication that may have originated $\times$ as the multiplication sign):

30 and 5

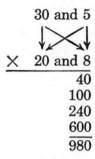

$\times$ 20 and 8

40
100
240
600
―――
980

Still higher numbers are treated the same. The system of multiplying each above by each below gets complicated and even when we use the mechanical method taught in school, it is possible to get lost, as you may see if you try to follow the multiplications below:

3965
$\times$ 2197
―――――
27755
35685
3965
7930
―――――
8711105

Still you will have to admit that this is an improvement over adding 3965 + 3965 + 3965 + 3965 + 3965 ... for 2197 times.

MULTIPLICATION IN REVERSE

Just as addition has its opposite in subtraction, so multiplication has its opposite in a type of number

manipulation called "division." Whereas multiplication is a kind of repeated addition, division is a
kind of repeated subtraction.

For instance, suppose you want to divide 15 by 3,
a process which can be symbolized as $15 \div 3$, $\div$
being the "division sign" (of uncertain origin).
One way of doing it is to subtract 3's over and over.
Thus $15 - 3 = 12$; $12 - 3 = 9$; $9 - 3 = 6$; $6 -$
$3 = 3$; and $3 - 3 = 0$. Or, to condense this,
$15 - 3 - 3 - 3 - 3 - 3 = 0$. You see that there
have been five subtractions; therefore $15 \div 3 = 5$.

However, this is never the way it is done. Instead, use is made of advance knowledge of the
results of multiplication. After all, if 15 is divided
by 3 to give some number, that number multiplied
by 3 must give you back your 15. You have gone
forward and then backward and must end in your
original place. (This is similar to the situation in
addition and subtraction, also reverse processes.
If $7 - 4 = 3$, then $3 + 4 = 7$.)

Consequently, when presented with a problem
like $15 \div 3$, what you are taught to do is to ask
yourself: What number multiplied by 3 will give 15?
From the multiplication table (which you have been
whipped and beaten into memorizing), you know
the number is 5 and that is your answer. In fact,
you generally know your multiplication table so

well that you automatically say "Five" in answer to the problem without giving the matter any conscious thought.

Since $5 \times 3 = 3 \times 5$, both coming to 15, it follows that $15 \div 5 = 3$ and $15 \div 3 = 5$. The same item in the multiplication table serves to give you the answer to both problems in division.*

The fact that division is worked backward, however, makes it more difficult than the other arithmetical operations, a fact the grade school youngster well knows.

Suppose, for instance, it were necessary to divide 7715 by 5. Counting the number of times you would have to subtract 5 from 7715 to reach 0 would be tedious, and the multiplication table certainly doesn't tell you what number must be multiplied by 5 to give you 7715.

But here's where multiplication by 0 comes in handy again. You know that $1 \times 5 = 5$, therefore

---

* Notice that in division, as in subtraction, the order of the numbers is important. Although 5×3 is equal to 3×5, $15 \div 5$ is by no means the same as $5 \div 15$. The number to the left of the division sign is the *dividend* (from a Latin word meaning "that which is divided") while the number to the right is the *divisor* ("that which is dividing"). The result of a division — that is, the answer to the question: "How many times does one number go into another?" — is the *quotient* (from a Latin word meaning "how many times?"). In the example, $15 \div 5 = 3$, 15 is the dividend, 5 the divisor, and 3 the quotient.

$1000 \times 5 = 5000$. That is as close as you can get to 7715, using nothing more than single digits and zeros, but it still leaves 2715. So you divide that by 5. The multiplication table tells you that 5×5 is 25 so $500 \times 5 = 2500$, and that leaves only 215. Try for that next. Since $4 \times 5 = 20$, then $40 \times 5 = 200$. That leaves only 15 and dividing that by 5 is easy. We know the answer is 3.

Altogether 5 has been multiplied first by 1000, then by 500, then by 40 and lastly by 3. Add that together and you find that 5 was multiplied by 1543 all told. Since $1543 \times 5 = 7715$, then $7715 \div 5 = 1543$ and that is our answer or quotient.

Again, youngsters are taught to do division by rote, and the problem just concluded would look like this, using the school method:

$$\begin{array}{r} 1543 \\ 5\overline{)7715} \\ 5 \\ \hline 27 \\ 25 \\ \hline 21 \\ 20 \\ \hline 15 \\ 15 \\ \hline 0 \end{array}$$

Dividing by numbers over 10 is more complicated, although the principle is unchanged. Because the multiplication table doesn't go above 10, we have to guess at answers sometimes and "try" them to see how they work out. That is the real difficulty with that bugbear of "long division." (Actually, though, students should consider themselves lucky. Before Arabic numbers were adopted, "long division" was very advanced mathematics that only a few mathematicians could master.)

THE PATTERN OF SIGNS

So far in this chapter I haven't mentioned negative numbers. Since they fit in so nicely in addition and subtraction, it would be pleasant to have them find a place in multiplication and division, too.

For instance, suppose you wished to multiply $(+3)$ and (-4). How would that work?

Well, consider three people, each one of whom has a $4 debt. To find the total debt we must add $4 + $4 + $4 and we find that altogether our three friends have a debt of $12.

Now adding three 4's is exactly what we have decided to call 3×4. Since the 4 in this case we have just considered is a $4 debt, it represents a -4, really, so that our problem reduces to $(+3) \times (-4)$. Since we have decided that the answer is a $12 debt, it seems that $(+3) \times (-4) = (-12)$.

The same result would have been obtained if we were considering four people each possessing a $3 debt. In other words $(+4) \times (-3) = (-12)$. And since it doesn't matter in which order numbers are multiplied, $(-4) \times (+3) = (-12)$ and $(-3) \times (+4) = (-12)$.

We can generalize. When two numbers, one negative and one positive, are multiplied, the answer is always negative. Numerically, the answer is the same as though both numbers were positive. Thus, the product of $(+4)$ and $(+3)$ is $(+12)$. The presence of a negative doesn't affect the numerical value of the product, only its sign.

Now what if *both* numbers are negative? Unfortunately, it is difficult to think up a handy practical case that would involve two negative numbers. Debts of $3 or $4 apiece are easy to imagine, but how can you dig up -4 or -3 men to have them?

Instead, let's tackle it another way. In multiplication, so far, changing one sign of the two numbers being multiplied has served to change the sign of the answer. Changing the signs of *both* numbers ought to change the sign of the answer *twice:* from positive to negative and then from negative back to positive again. (After all, if you about-face twice, you find yourself facing in the original direction again.)

Consequently, it is logical (although a little strange) to state that $(-3) \times (-4) = (+12)$.

The pattern of signs in multiplication is this then:

$$\text{positive} \times \text{positive} = \text{positive}$$
$$\text{negative} \times \text{positive} = \text{negative}$$
$$\text{positive} \times \text{negative} = \text{negative}$$
$$\text{negative} \times \text{negative} = \text{positive}$$

In short, multiplying like signs yields positive; multiplying unlike signs yields negative.

What's more, these same rules hold for multiplication's opposite, division. Thus $(+12) \div (+4) = (+3)$; $(+12) \div (-4) = (-3)$; $(-12) \div (+4) = (-3)$; and $(-12) \div (-4) = (+3)$.

You can check this by reversing the divisions into multiplication again. If, in each of the divisions above, you multiply the quotient by the smaller number on the left (the divisor), you will get the larger number (the dividend), complete with the proper sign. If you reverse the second division, for instance, you get $(-3) \times (-4) = (+12)$.

TO DIVIDE OR NOT TO DIVIDE

When division is defined as repeated subtraction until zero is reached, it turns out that division is sometimes impossible. For instance, what is $7 \div 2$?

By repeated subtraction, we can say that $7 - 2 - 2 - 2 = 1$, but there we have to stop. If we subtract a fourth 2, we go below zero. Even if we recognize the existence of negative numbers (which the ancients did not), we can't allow the subtraction to go below zero. The next subtraction would reach −1, another would reach −3, then −5, and so on forever. Where would we stop? The whole system would break down.

Suppose we look at it another way. To solve 7 ÷ 2, we might think of the multiplication table and ask ourselves: What number multiplied by 2 gives 7? As it turns out, there is no such number in the multiplication table, if we take into account only the type of number we have so far been considering. To be sure $3 \times 2 = 6$ and $4 \times 2 = 8$, but there is no number which can be multiplied by 2 to give 7.

It follows then that as long as we define division in this manner, some divisions are possible and some are impossible. Ancient peoples, especially the Greeks, were fascinated by this, and looked for patterns in it.

For instance, what numbers can be divided by 2? It turns out that every other number can be. The numeral 1 can't be, 2 can, 3 can't, 4 can, 5 can't, and so on.

Numbers were early differentiated into those that could be divided by 2 and those that could not. Early Greek mathematicians delighted in finding mystic significance in this. Some considered numbers divisible by 2 to be female and unlucky, while the others were male and lucky. (Greek mathematicians were all males and prejudiced in favor of males.)

In everyday life, the question of divisibility by 2 impressed ordinary people whenever it became necessary to share a fixed number of objects among two persons. Share-and-share-alike is often the best way to avoid a quarrel.

The simplest way of sharing in days when the knowledge of division among ordinary folk must have been shaky would be to make two piles by placing one object in each pile alternately. If we imagine that these are objects which can be stacked neatly, such as checkers, then, if the original number was divisible by 2, we would end with the same number of checkers in each pile. If we had started with 16 checkers, there would be 8 in each pile. The two piles, placed side by side, would be evenly matched; hence 16 (or any number divisible by 2) is an "even" number.

If, however, we started with 17 checkers, the two piles would not come out evenly. By the time 16 checkers had been distributed, we would find two equal piles with one checker left over. Whichever pile we chose to place that last checker upon would stick up higher than the other. It would form a

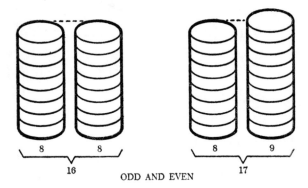

ODD AND EVEN

point, so to speak. An old Teutonic word meaning "a point" was "oddi;" hence 17 (or any number not divisible by 2) is an "odd" number.

Divisibility or nondivisibility by other numbers also forms patterns. No pattern, however, is as simple and as easily grasped as is the odd-even alternation.

THE GREEKS AMUSE THEMSELVES

Another early discovery about division was the fact that some numbers could be divided by more than one smaller number. For instance, 60 can be divided by 2, 3, 4, 5, 6, 10, 12, 15, 20, and 30. Each of these numbers is capable of dividing 60 evenly and is called a "factor" of 60. It follows that 60 has ten different factors.

To be sure, there are two other factors that I

haven't mentioned. One is 60 itself. After all, $60 \div 60 = 1$. In fact, any number divided by itself is 1, so that any number is one of its own factors. The remaining factor is 1, since $60 \div 1 = 60$. Again, any number can be divided by 1, leaving itself unchanged, so that 1 is a kind of universal factor.

Because any number can be divided by itself and by 1, the Greeks (who loved to play games with factors) usually disregarded those two numbers as factors. There is no interesting pattern, after all, in something that hits all numbers without distinction. (Incidentally, for every factor a number has, there is another that is the negative of the first. For instance, 60 can be divided by -2, -3, -4, and so on. The Greeks, however, didn't recognize negative numbers, and they don't really introduce anything new, so we usually disregard them as factors, also.)

Now, then, although 60 has ten factors, near-by numbers are not as fortunate. The number 58 has only two factors, 2 and 29; while 62 also only has two factors, 2 and 31.

However, no matter how few factors a number may have, as long as factors exist, that number is called a "composite number" because it can be looked upon as being composed of smaller numbers multiplied together. The number 58 can be looked upon as being 2×29, and the number 62 as 2×31.

The number 60 is more complicated because it has several factors. It could, for instance, be expressed as 2×30, but 30 is itself a composite number which can be expressed as 2×15, and 15 is a composite number, being 3×5. The final breakdown then expresses 60 as $2 \times 2 \times 3 \times 5$.

In the two paragraphs above, no attempt is made to break down 2, 3, 5, or, for that matter, 29 and 31 into factors. The reason for that is they have none (other than themselves and 1, of course). In other words, no number, other than themselves and 1, exists which will divide them evenly.

Numbers without factors, such as 2, 3, 5, 7, 11, 13, 17, 19, and so on, are called "prime numbers" or simply "primes" from a Latin word meaning "first." To people who see mystical values in numbers, you see, it might seem as though the prime numbers would have to exist first, while the composite numbers could be built up afterward out of the primes. Once 2, 3, and 5 existed, in other words, 60 could be formed by multiplying $2 \times 2 \times 3 \times 5$.

It might seem that as one went higher and higher in the scale of numbers, the possibility of primes would vanish, since there would be more and more lower numbers to choose from as possible factors.

This, however, is not true. The Greek mathematician Euclid proved 2200 years ago that there is no such thing as a highest prime number. No matter how high a prime number might be, he showed how one could devise a still higher one that was also prime.

The Greeks played all sorts of games with factors. For instance, they would add up the factors of numbers (including 1 this time, but excluding the number itself) to see what would happen. Sometimes the factors of a number added up to less than the number itself. For instance, the factors of 10 (1, 2, and 5) add up to only 8. The number 10, therefore, they called a "deficient number." The factors of 12 (1, 2, 3, 4, and 6), on the other hand, add up to 16, more than the number itself, so 12 they called an "abundant number."

The factors of 6 (1, 2, and 3), however, add up to 6, and the factors of 28 (1, 2, 4, 7, and 14) add up to 28. These, the Greeks called "perfect numbers."

Still further, the factors of 220 (1, 2, 4, 5, 10, 11, 20, 22, 44, 55, and 110) add up to 284, while the factors of 284 (1, 2, 4, 71, and 142) add up to 220. These are said to be "amicable numbers."

This division of numbers into prime, perfect, amicable, and so on, has never been of much practical importance but it has fascinated mathematicians for thousands of years, and it still does.

COUNTING AND MEASURING

So far, I have been talking about the numbers we get by counting: 1, 2, 3, and so on. Those numbers and the manipulations involving them (as so far discussed) are sometimes all we need.

For instance, the boys in a classroom can be represented by a number. There are 4 boys or 5 boys or some other number. It is always a definite number, however. You cannot, for instance, say, after a close and judicious examination: "Well, there are more than four boys, that's plain; but there are definitely less than five boys. I guess it's something in between four and five boys."

There is no number between 4 and 5 if you are counting objects. It's either 4 boys or 5 boys and there is no in-between. Furthermore, if you start with 4 boys and 2 more come in, the result is 6 boys. Not a trifle over 6 or a hair under 6, but exactly 6.

However, suppose you asked another question, one like this: "How many hours have those boys been studying?"

In that case, you might easily answer, "They have studied more than one hour, I'm sure, but certainly less than two hours."

Here such an answer would make sense. There *is* such a thing as a length of time that is more than 1 hour and less than 2 hours. Time is not something you count but something you measure.

Counting and measuring must be handled differently. In counting, you are dealing with separate or "discrete" objects. The numbers we have been discussing are themselves separate and discrete and so they can be matched nicely against the objects. They are all we need.

The act of measuring something that does not consist of separate objects, however, is another matter entirely. There we are dealing with something that is "continuous." We must deal with a continuous stretch of time, for instance; or a continuous length of line.

Ordinary numbers, which are discrete, cannot be made to match something that is continuous without the danger of running into trouble, as in the case of the problem above concerning the number of hours that the boys had been studying.

To avoid such problems, the numbers must be made continuous. The space between ordinary numbers must be filled up with "in-between" numbers. When this is done, the numbers 1, 2, 3, and so on, become merely a small part of a continuous system which can then be matched against time, length or any other continuous phenomenon that must be measured.

Beginning with the next chapter, we'll see how these in-between numbers arose, and how they are handled.

4
4
4
Broken Numbers
4

IN A PRACTICAL SENSE, mankind could not afford to recognize any limitations in division. Suppose it were necessary to divide two apples among four children. No use saying that 2 cannot be divided by 4 because there is no number in the multiplication table which, when multiplied by 4, will give 2. What the practical mother does is to divide each apple into two equal pieces and then give each of the four waiting children a piece of apple. (Or make applesauce, perhaps.)

Following this system, mankind broke up his common measuring units into smaller pieces, and gave the smaller pieces names also. For instance, in our own system of measures, a quart of liquid can be divided up into two equal parts called pints. If you have two quarts and four men waiting, each man gets a pint.

You can divide units into greater numbers of subunits, too. A bushel can be divided into 4 pecks and a peck into 8 quarts. An avoirdupois pound can be divided into 16 avoirdupois ounces, while a quart can be divided into 32 fluid ounces. All these figures are the result of dividing something into two pieces, then each piece into two more, then each smaller piece into two more and so on.

You could, for instance, divide a quart among two men by giving each 16 fluid ounces (which equals a pint, by the way), or you can give four men 8 fluid ounces each (a half pint), or eight men 4 fluid ounces each (a gill), or sixteen men 2 fluid ounces each (a half gill), or 32 men 1 fluid ounce each.

This sounds pretty good, but what do you do if you have three men waiting in line? A 32-ounce quart cannot be divided among three men with each man getting an even number of ounces, since 3 is not a factor of 32. Yet 3 men are much more likely to want to share a quart than are 16 men, or 32.

It is useful, therefore, to pick some subunit that involves as many factors as possible among the lower numbers. Take 12 for instance. We have 12 inches in a foot, 12 troy ounces in a troy pound and 12 anything in a dozen, for that matter.

Observe how useful the dozen is. If you have a dozen apples, you can divide them equally into 2 groups of 6 each, 3 groups of 4 each, 4 groups of 3 each, 6 groups of 2 each, or 12 groups of 1 each.

The important thing is that not only are 2 and 4 factors of 12, but 3 is also.

Then, too, a manufacturer selling by the dozen can sell in smaller groups without too much difficulty in adjusting prices because there are so many ways he can divide up the dozen evenly. There is also a dozen dozen or a "gross," representing 12 × 12 or 144 items. The factors of 144 are 2, 3, 4, 6, 8, 9, 12, 16, 18, 24, 36, 48, and 72.

The convenience of such factoring in practical arithmetic is great, and there are people who wish that we had used 12 as the base of our number system instead of 10. The number 10 has only two factors, 2 and 5, and cannot be divided evenly by either 3 or 4. The only reason 10 won out over 12 is probably the anatomical accident that we have 5 fingers on each hand. Now if we had had 6 on each hand —

There is one advantage, though, that 10 has over 12. The number 5 is a factor of 10 but not of 12. The ancient Babylonians tried to combine the good features of 10 and 12 by finding a number for which not only 2, 3, and 4, but also 5 was a factor. The smallest such number is 60.

Astronomy sided with the Babylonians in this respect. The year is 365 days (and a few hours) long. This is the length of time that the sun takes to make its (apparent) circuit about the skies against the background of the fixed stars. If this whole circle were divided into "day-journeys" of the sun, there would be 365 such pieces of a circle.

Now either the Babylonians had the number of days in a year a little wrong or, more likely, deliberately rounded the number to 360. In their system, you see, it was easy to handle 360, which is 60×6. So they divide the celestial sphere, and all other circles, too, into 360 equal parts we call "degrees" today. Furthermore, they divided each degree into 60 equal parts we call "minutes" and each minute into 60 equal parts we call "seconds."*

We still keep that Babylonian system. Furthermore, since time is measured by the movement of the heavenly bodies in the sky, our hour is divided

---

* The Latin word "degradus" means "steps down" and hence refers to something like a ladder or staircase, down which you can indeed step. Regular divisions resembling the steps of a ladder or staircase may therefore be called "degrees," which is a corruption of "degradus." Thus, we not only have degrees of a circle, but also degrees of temperature. The sixty divisions of a degree were first called "pars minuta prima" and the sixty divisions of each of these were "pars minuta secunda" meaning "first small part" and "second small part" respectively. The former phrase eventually got shortened to "minute" and the latter to "second."

into 60 minutes which in turn are divided into 60 seconds.

A trace of the 12-system also shows up in our time-telling. Our daytime and nighttime are both broken up into 12 hours. Originally, before the invention of clocks, these hours varied with the changing lengths of day and night with the seasons. In winter, the daytime hours would be short and the nighttime hours long, while in summer this was reversed. Nowadays, our hours are of equal length at all times so that in summer the daytime lasts longer than 12 hours and the nighttime less, while in winter this is reversed.

Nevertheless, our clocks still show only 12 numerals and we have to distinguish between

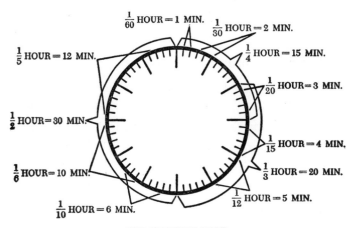

THE 60-MINUTE HOUR

1 A.M. and 1 P.M. (The armed forces have continued on from 12 noon and speak of 13:00, 14:00,
and so on, but this is not catching on among
civilians, apparently.)

PARTS OF ONE

What can be done for ordinary units of measure
by the average man, can be done for pure numbers
by mathematicians. Why not divide the numeral
1 into two equal parts, or three, or four, or any
number? In order to do that usefully, it is necessary,
first, to give these "parts of one" a name; second,
to find an appropriate symbol for the parts; and
third, to work out some system for handling these
parts in the usual arithmetical manipulations.

After all, if parts of numbers can be manipulated
like ordinary numbers, they can be considered ordinary numbers for all purposes, practical or theoretical.

The names are easy and come from the common
language. Two equal parts of anything are "halves"
(from an old Teutonic word meaning "to cut").
Parts resulting from division into larger numbers of
pieces are named after the "ordinal" form of those
numbers. That is, three parts of one are "thirds,"
four parts are "fourths," then "fifths," "sixths," and
as far as you care to go. (The one irregular possibility is that "fourths" are sometimes called "quar-

ters," from a Latin word meaning "four.")

A half is what results when a unit is divided into two pieces. In other words, it is $1 \div 2$. This gives rise to no ordinary number and there is no use looking for one. It is sufficient simply to indicate the operation in as direct a manner as possible and this is done by writing it $\frac{1}{2}$ or $1/2$. This can be read "one divided by two" or, more often, "one over two," or, still more often, simply "one-half."

Similarly, one-third is $\frac{1}{3}$, one-fifth is $\frac{1}{5}$, and so on. There is no attempt to "solve" the division; you simply state the division. To say that $1 \div 3 = \frac{1}{3}$ is to say no more than that "one divided by three is equal to one divided by three."

This may sound frustrating. You may ask: But what *is* one divided by three? The answer is: What's the difference? If $\frac{1}{3}$ can be manipulated as though it were the answer, why look any further?

These pieces of a unit are called "fractions," from a Latin word meaning "broken," since they are obtained by "breaking" 1 into pieces. Ordinary numbers are called "whole numbers" in contrast, or "integers," a Latin word meaning "whole."

Fractions can therefore also be looked upon as parts of whole numbers, or of whole things generally.

And now to consider the manipulation of fractions. Let's begin by asking if fractions can be added and subtracted, and, if so, how. Suppose we want to add $\frac{1}{3}$ and $\frac{1}{3}$. If we change that to words, it sounds simple. Here is one-third and there is one-third. Add them together and you obviously have two-thirds. (Just as one apple plus one apple is two apples.)

The next question is, How do you symbolize two-thirds? Since one-third is $\frac{1}{3}$, it seems logical to suppose that two-thirds ought to be $\frac{2}{3}$. We can test that. The symbol $\frac{1}{3}$ means "one divided by three," therefore $\frac{2}{3}$ ought to be "two divided by three."

But how do we go about dividing two by three? If we had two small pies and three children, we could do this by dividing each pie into three equal parts, giving us a total of 6 equal pie-parts, each equal to one-third of a pie. These 6 parts can be divided among 3 children by giving each drooling child 2 pieces, and each child ends up with two-thirds of a pie. Consequently, two-thirds *can* be

considered as the quotient of $2 \div 3$ and *can* be represented as $\frac{2}{3}$.

Using the same type of reasoning, you can show that any division can be represented as a fraction. Forty-three pies divided equally among seventy-three people will result in each person having $\frac{43}{73}$ of a pie.

But back to our addition and subtraction. As we reasoned with $\frac{1}{3} + \frac{1}{3}$, so we can reason that $\frac{1}{5} + \frac{1}{5} + \frac{1}{5} = \frac{3}{5}$ and that $\frac{3}{5} - \frac{2}{5} = \frac{1}{5}$.

We can make a general rule. In adding or subtracting fractions with equal "denominators" (the name given to the number of the fraction below the line, or on the right of the slant line which is sometimes used) it is only necessary to add or subtract the "numerators" (the name given to the upper number of the fraction, or the one on the left of the slant line).

The same holds true for multiplication and division of fractions by integers; only the numerator of the fraction is affected. The product of $\frac{1}{7}$ and 6 is $\frac{6}{7}$, while the quotient of $\frac{18}{23}$ divided by 9 is $\frac{2}{23}$; just as 1 apple multiplied by 6 is 6 apples and 18 apples divided by 9 is 2 apples.

It may happen in the process of adding to or multiplying a fraction that the numerator may become as large as or larger than the denominator. For instance, $\frac{1}{3} + \frac{1}{3} + \frac{1}{3}$ gives the answer $\frac{3}{3}$, as does $\frac{1}{3} \times 3$. What is the significance of $\frac{3}{3}$? Obviously, if you divide a unit into three equal pieces, then take the sum of all three thirds, you have your original unit back again. In other words, $\frac{3}{3}$ is 1; and this fits in with the way in which we have defined a fraction, since $3 \div 3$ is indeed 1.

In the same way $\frac{2}{2}$, $\frac{4}{4}$, $\frac{27}{27}$, or $\frac{109476}{109476}$ are all equal to 1.

But what if $\frac{1}{3}$ is multiplied by 4 so that the answer is $\frac{4}{3}$? What is the significance of $\frac{4}{3}$? Well, $\frac{4}{3}$ can be looked at as being $\frac{3}{3} + \frac{1}{3}$. The quantity $\frac{3}{3}$ we already know is 1, so $\frac{4}{3}$ must be equal to $1 + \frac{1}{3}$, and this is written $1\frac{1}{3}$ or 1 1/3, which is read "one and one-third."

In school we are usually taught to change as much of the fraction as possible into integers, so that we get into the habit of changing $\frac{4}{3}$ into $1\frac{1}{3}$ and $\frac{27}{5}$ into $5\frac{2}{5}$ and so on. There is no real reason to have to do this. As a matter of fact, $\frac{4}{3}$ and $\frac{27}{5}$ are easier to manipulate than $1\frac{1}{3}$ and $5\frac{2}{5}$. It is just the natural conservatism of a world that has had to accept fractions when they were accustomed for so long to whole numbers only.

In fact, fractions with values less than 1 (that is, with the numerator smaller numerically than the denominator) are called "proper fractions." Those equal to or greater than 1 (that is, those with the numerator equal to or greater than the denominator) are, however, called, with a faint flavor of disapproval, "improper fractions."

Nevertheless, it is important to remember that all fractions can be handled in identical fashion. All are equally "proper" from the mathematical standpoint.

THE DENOMINATOR JOINS THE GAME

Suppose we consider the fraction $\frac{6}{3}$. In value, it is equal to 2, as you can see by converting $\frac{6}{3}$ into $6 \div 3$.

Now what happens if we multiply both numerator and denominator by 2, changing the $\frac{6}{3}$ into $\frac{12}{6}$? Obviously, nothing at all happens to the value of the fraction, since $12 \div 6$ is still 2. Or we could multiply the numerator and denominator of $\frac{6}{3}$ by 3 to get $\frac{18}{9}$; or by 27 to get $\frac{162}{81}$; or by 101 to get $\frac{606}{303}$. In every case, the value of the fraction, as obtained by division, is still 2, and therefore unchanged.

The same thing would happen if we had started with $\frac{120}{60}$ (equal to 2) and divided both numerator and denominator by 2 $\left(\text{to get }\frac{60}{30}\right)$ or 3 $\left(\text{to get }\frac{40}{20}\right)$ or

$4 \left(\text{to get } \dfrac{30}{15}\right)$ and so on. In every case, the **value** would remain unchanged.

Nor would matters be different if we were **dealing** with a fraction that was not equal to an integer in value. If $\dfrac{1}{3}$ is multiplied top and bottom by 2 to form $\dfrac{2}{6}$, there is no change. If you divided a pie into 3 equal pieces and took 1 piece, or divided it into 6 equal pieces and took 2, you would end **up** with the same quantity of pie each time. **Conse-** quently, $\dfrac{1}{3}$ and $\dfrac{2}{6}$ are identical.

The general rule, then, is that any fraction **can** have its numerator and denominator multiplied **or** divided by the same number without change **in** value. This can be a useful rule in several **ways.** For instance, it enables you to dispense sometimes (but not always) with high numbers.

For example, the fraction $\dfrac{126}{189}$ can be divided, **top** and bottom, by 63, and if that is done, it becomes the familiar $\dfrac{2}{3}$. Again, $\dfrac{155}{31}$, divided top and bottom by 31, becomes $\dfrac{5}{1}$, which is equal to 5, since $5 \div 1 = 5$.

This is my first mention of fractions with a **de-**

nominator of 1, and these are unusually important. Remember that any number divided by 1 remains unchanged in value; this means that any fraction with a denominator of 1 is equal to its numerator in value. Thus, $\frac{273}{1} = 273$; $\frac{509993}{1} = 509993$, and so on. For this reason, we don't have to divide up numbers into integers and fractions. We can consider all numbers as fractions by converting all integers into fractions with the numerator equal to the integer itself and the denominator equal to one.

Such "denominator-one" fractions can be manipulated in the same way as other fractions: $\frac{15}{1} + \frac{15}{1} = \frac{30}{1}$; $\frac{4}{1} \times \frac{3}{1} = \frac{12}{1}$.

You may wonder, then, what the advantage is of adding an apparently unnecessary line and denominator to perfectly satisfactory integers. The answer to that is that it enables integers and fractions to take part in arithmetical operations together with greater ease.

For instance, how would you add $\frac{1}{3}$ and $\frac{1}{5}$? So far, we have been adding only fractions with the same denominators, so it would seem that we ought to find a way to convert these fractions into other fractions that have the same denominators. Here's where multiplication top and bottom is useful again.

First we multiply $\frac{1}{3}$ by 5, top and bottom. This gives us $\frac{5}{15}$ and does not change the value of the fraction. Then we multiply $\frac{1}{5}$ by 3, top and bottom, to get $\frac{3}{15}$, again without changing its value. Therefore, $\frac{1}{3} + \frac{1}{5}$ is the same as $\frac{5}{15} + \frac{3}{15}$, and the latter is easy to handle. The answer is obviously $\frac{8}{15}$.

Now we can follow the same system in additions that involve both integers and fractions, if we change integers into "denominator-one" fractions. To add $3 + \frac{1}{3} + 1\frac{1}{4}$, we first convert all into fractions: $\frac{3}{1} + \frac{1}{3} + \frac{5}{4}$. We then multiply each fraction, top and bottom, in such a way as to end with fractions of equal denominator; the first fraction by 12, the second by 4, and the third by 3. This gives us $\frac{36}{12} + \frac{4}{12} + \frac{15}{12}$ which adds up to $\frac{55}{12}$.

If you disapprove of improper fractions, $\frac{55}{12}$ can be converted to $\frac{48}{12} + \frac{7}{12}$ or, $4\frac{7}{12}$.

FRACTIONS BELOW ZERO

Everything I have said about fractions so far will hold perfectly well in the negative numbers. Thus $-1 \div 3$ can be written $\frac{-1}{3}$, and $1 \div -3$ can be written $\frac{1}{-3}$. In either case (since negative divided by positive, and positive divided by negative each gives a negative quotient) the entire fraction can be considered negative and written simply $-\frac{1}{3}$. Here the minus sign applies to the fraction as a whole and not to either numerator or denominator particularly.

On the other hand, $-1 \div -3$ can be written $\frac{-1}{-3}$. And since negative divided by negative gives a positive quotient, $\frac{-1}{-3}$ can be considered as $+\frac{1}{3}$.

Negative fractions are involved in addition and subtraction on the same basis as positive fractions. For instance, what is $1 - 1\frac{1}{3}$? Changing both into fractions, we have $\frac{1}{1} - \frac{4}{3}$. To get similar denominators, we multiply $\frac{1}{1}$ by 3, top and bottom. This leaves us $\frac{3}{3} - \frac{4}{3}$ and the answer is $-\frac{1}{3}$.

5
5
5
Breakage by Tens
5

AVOIDING DIVISION

WE ARE BY NO MEANS DONE with fractions.
So far we have multiplied and divided fractions only
by integers. Is it possible to multiply and divide
fractions by fractions; and if so, how?

Suppose we break up $\frac{1}{3}$ into two equal pieces.
Three thirds, taken together, would be 1. If each
third is broken in two, it takes 6 of the smaller
pieces to make 1. Each of these smaller pieces is
therefore one-sixth, and we can say that one-half
of one-third is one-sixth.

By the same reasoning one-half of one-fourth is
one-eighth, and one-third of one-fourth is one-
twelfth.

A convenient way of symbolizing this is to write:
$\frac{1}{3} \times \frac{1}{2} = \frac{1}{6}$; $\frac{1}{4} \times \frac{1}{2} = \frac{1}{8}$; and $\frac{1}{3} \times \frac{1}{4} = \frac{1}{12}$. The
multiplication sign is used because we seem to
get the right answer in each case if we multiply the
two denominators. What about the numerators,

though? The 1 seems untouched but, on the other hand, $1 \times 1 = 1$. To answer the question, let's try fractions with numerators other than 1.

Suppose we break up 10 into 5 equal pieces. Each piece is one-fifth of 10. Since $10 \div 5 = 2$, it must be that one-fifth of ten is 2. The phrase "one-fifth of ten" can be written $\frac{1}{5} \times 10$, but let's convert it into fractions. First, $\frac{1}{5}$ can be converted to $\frac{2}{10}$ by multiplying by 2, top and bottom, in order to make the numerator something other than 1. Then 10 can be converted to $\frac{10}{1}$, which by multiplying top and bottom by 3 can be made to equal $\frac{30}{3}$.

We can say then that $\frac{1}{5} \times 10$ is the same as $\frac{2}{10} \times \frac{30}{3}$. If we multiply the latter fractions, numerator by numerator and denominator by denominator, we get $\frac{2 \times 30}{10 \times 3}$ or $\frac{60}{30}$ or 2. This is the answer we expected.

Or suppose in the multiplication $\frac{1}{3} \times \frac{1}{2}$, we had converted the fractions to $\frac{4}{12}$ and $\frac{6}{12}$, as we might by multiplying the first, top and bottom, by 4 and the second by 6. Now $\frac{4}{12} \times \frac{6}{12}$ equals $\frac{24}{144}$ if we follow the numerator-times-numerator, denominator-times-denominator system. By dividing the answer, $\frac{24}{144}$, by 24, top and bottom, we come out with $\frac{1}{6}$, which we have decided is the correct answer for $\frac{1}{3} \times \frac{1}{2}$.

Division works similarly. Numerator must be divided by numerator; denominator by denominator. Thus, $\frac{10}{21} \div \frac{5}{7}$ equals $\frac{10 \div 5}{21 \div 7}$ or $\frac{2}{3}$. Here, however, a complication enters. What if numerator doesn't go into numerator evenly or denominator into denominator (or both)? Suppose you try to divide $\frac{5}{7}$ by $\frac{2}{3}$. Both numerator and denominator will end up fractions; there would be fractions within fractions.

Fortunately such division can be avoided.

Let's go back to our problem of breaking up 10 into 5 equal pieces. We got the same answer, 2, whether we wrote $10 \div 5$ or $10 \times \frac{1}{5}$. Now 5 can be written $\frac{5}{1}$, and $\frac{5}{1}$, so to speak, is $\frac{1}{5}$ standing on its head. Two fractions which resemble one another except that the numerator of one is the denominator of the other and vice versa are said to be "reciprocal fractions." The word "reciprocal" comes from a Latin term meaning "to turn in the opposite direction." Certainly $\frac{5}{1}$ is $\frac{1}{5}$ "turned in the opposite direction." Thus, 5 is the reciprocal of $\frac{1}{5}$, and $\frac{1}{5}$ is the reciprocal of 5. Furthermore, $\frac{2}{3}$ is the reciprocal of $\frac{3}{2}$; $\frac{55}{26}$ is the reciprocal of $\frac{26}{55}$, and so on.

Well, then, when we say that $10 \div 5$ gives the same answer as $10 \times \frac{1}{5}$, it looks as though dividing by a number may be the same as multiplying by its reciprocal. (Notice that, in this process, it is always the divisor, never the dividend, that is made into its reciprocal.) Let's try another case. Just above I said that $\frac{10}{21} \div \frac{5}{7}$ was equal to $\frac{2}{3}$. Suppose, instead, that we made it $\frac{10}{21} \times \frac{7}{5}$. The answer would be $\frac{70}{105}$. Dividing that fraction, top and bottom, by

35, gives us $\frac{2}{3}$, which is the same answer.

Now we may divide $\frac{5}{7}$ by $\frac{2}{3}$ without the danger of fractions within fractions by multiplying, instead, $\frac{5}{7} \times \frac{3}{2}$. The answer is $\frac{15}{14}$.

Furthermore, in multiplying fractions, we should remember that the order in which numbers are multiplied makes no difference. For instance, multiplying $\frac{10}{21} \times \frac{7}{5}$ is the same as multiplying $\frac{10}{5}$ by $\frac{7}{21}$. In the first case the answer is $\frac{10 \times 7}{21 \times 5}$ and in the second $\frac{10 \times 7}{5 \times 21}$. In either case, it works out to $\frac{70}{105}$, or (dividing top and bottom by 35) $\frac{2}{3}$.

But there is an advantage in the second arrangement. The fractions $\frac{10}{21}$ and $\frac{7}{5}$ cannot be reduced to any simpler form, but $\frac{10}{5}$ is convertible at a glance to $\frac{2}{1}$, while $\frac{7}{21}$ is easily seen to be equal to $\frac{1}{3}$. The problem $\frac{10}{5} \times \frac{7}{21}$ is changed into $\frac{2}{1} \times \frac{1}{3}$, which

equals $\frac{2}{3}$.

The usefulness of working with smaller numbers whenever possible leads to the routine division of top and bottom whenever fractions are multiplied without even bothering to rearrange. Thus, in the problem $\frac{7}{10} \times \frac{17}{49}$, the numerator of one fraction and the denominator of the other are divided by 7 so that the problem now reads $\frac{1}{10} \times \frac{17}{7}$. In either case, the answer comes out $\frac{17}{70}$, but it is easier to get that answer out of the second version.

The convenience of "reducing to lowest terms" or "factoring" when fractions are multiplied leads the hopeful student to attempt the same trick when fractions are added. Here, it won't work. The sum of $\frac{7}{10} + \frac{17}{49}$ is *not* the same as that of $\frac{1}{10} + \frac{17}{7}$. The first sum is $\frac{513}{490}$ and the second is $\frac{1239}{490}$.

The trouble here is that before you can do anything in the way of adding fractions, you must equalize the denominators. In the case of $\frac{7}{10} + \frac{17}{49}$, this can be done by multiplying the first fraction, top and bottom, by 49 and the second by 10 so as to get $\frac{343}{490} + \frac{170}{490}$. Once you have done that, factoring is still useless because it will throw your denominators out of line again. So in the addition of fractions, forget about factoring.

FORCING FRACTIONS INTO LINE

It must be admitted, though, that there is something not very pretty about fractions. Whether "one and a half" is written 1 1/2 or $1\frac{1}{2}$ or $1\frac{1}{2}$, the fraction breaks up the smooth flow and beautiful logic of positional notation.

The number 3184 $\frac{3}{4}$ means, if we go by our positional values, 3 "thousands" plus 1 "hundred" plus 8 "tens" plus 4 "ones" plus 3 "fourths." Until that miserable fraction we have been letting each place have a value one-tenth that of the place to its left. Why can't we continue this past the "ones" place?

In other words, $1000 \times \frac{1}{10} = 100$; $100 \times \frac{1}{10} = 10$; and $10 \times \frac{1}{10} = 1$. That's fine, so far, but why not continue, as follows: $1 \times \frac{1}{10} = \frac{1}{10}$; $\frac{1}{10} \times \frac{1}{10} =$

$\frac{1}{100}$; $\frac{1}{100} \times \frac{1}{10} = \frac{1}{1000}$ and so on. Thus, by using one system steadily we go past the "ones" position in the number into "tenths," "hundredths," "thousandths," and so on.

Let's consider the fraction $\frac{1}{2}$. Multiplying top and bottom by 5, it turns out we can express it just as well by saying $\frac{5}{10}$. A number like $55 \frac{1}{2}$ can therefore be changed to $55 \frac{5}{10}$ or to 55.5. This number is read "fifty-five point five," the point being placed immediately after the "ones" place so as to separate integers from fractions. Positionally, then, 55.5 can be read as 5 "tens" plus 5 "ones" plus 5 "tenths."

The fraction $\frac{3}{4}$ can be converted, by multiplying top and bottom by 25, to $\frac{75}{100}$. This is equal to $\frac{70}{100} + \frac{5}{100}$ or to $\frac{7}{10} + \frac{5}{100}$. The number $55 \frac{3}{4}$ can therefore be written as 55.75 (5 "tens" plus 5 "ones" plus 7 "tenths" plus 5 "hundredths").

Fractions which are in the form of so many tenths or hundredths or thousandths are called "decimal fractions," from a Latin word for "ten." When decimal fractions are welded into line, making use of positional notation, the results, like 55.5 and 55.75, are called "decimals" and the point used to mark off integers from fractions is the "decimal point."

A decimal fraction that is less than one, such as $\frac{7}{10}$, must be written entirely to the right of the decimal point, as .7. The danger of losing the exposed dot is considerable and mistaking .7 for 7 could introduce quite an error. It is customary, therefore, to write .7 as 0.7 (zero "ones" plus 7 "tenths" is the same as saying, simply, 7 "tenths") just to protect the decimal point. One might also write $\frac{7}{10}$ as 0.70 or 0.700 or 0.700000000. The addition of 0 "hundredths" plus 0 "thousandths" and so on does not change the numerical value of the original 0.7.

The great advantage of the decimal system is that in adding and subtracting you can forget all about fractions and deal as though only integers were involved. On the abacus, for instance, you needn't make the bottom rung "ones." You can make the middle rung "ones" and let those above be "tens," "hundreds," "thousands," and so on, while those below are "tenths," "hundredths," "thousandths,"

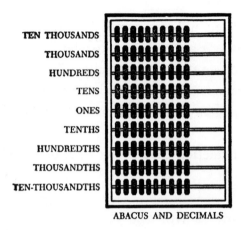

TEN THOUSANDS
THOUSANDS
HUNDREDS
TENS
ONES
TENTHS
HUNDREDTHS
THOUSANDTHS
TEN-THOUSANDTHS

ABACUS AND DECIMALS

and so on. The ordinary abacus manipulations will work all up and down the line whether in thousands or thousandths.

In pencil and paper addition, the same is true. Suppose we wanted to add $1\frac{1}{2} + 1\frac{3}{4}$, keeping fractions. First, we would change the numbers to $\frac{3}{2} + \frac{7}{4}$, then to $\frac{6}{4} + \frac{7}{4}$, which comes to $\frac{13}{4}$, which would then be changed to $3\frac{1}{4}$.

But suppose that we use decimals instead. The number $1\frac{1}{2}$ is 1.5 while $1\frac{3}{4}$ is 1.75. We add them as follows:

$$\begin{array}{r} 1.50 \\ +\ 1.75 \\ \hline 3.25 \end{array}$$

(Notice that I have written 1.5 as 1.50 so as to have something in the hundredths column, since there is a number in the hundredths column of the other decimal. Leaving out that 0 increases the chance of having beginners write

$$\begin{array}{r} 1.5 \\ +\ 1.75 \end{array}$$

which would create trouble.)

The answer to the decimal version is 3.25 which is 3 plus $\frac{2}{10}$ plus $\frac{5}{100}$. This, if you care to work out the addition, comes to $3\frac{1}{4}$, the answer we know to be correct.

Actually, though, there is no necessity to keep switching back and forth from fractions to decimals. Once the decimal notation is firmly fixed in the mind, it is possible to work entirely with decimals and be comfortable with them.

AMERICAN SENSE AND NONSENSE

An example of the comfortable use of the decimal system is found in the American system of coinage. Our coinage is decimal in nature since 10 mills equal 1 cent; 10 cents equal 1 dime; 10 dimes equal 1 dollar; and 10 dollars equal 1 eagle. (To be sure, we practically never made use of mills and eagles but the principle remains.) *

Thus we can always write money in decimals. If you have $13.26 in your pocket, you may have 1 ten-dollar bill, 3 one-dollar bills, 2 tenths-of-a-dollar (dimes) and 6 hundredths-of-a-dollar (cents).

You may not, of course. You may instead have 1 five-dollar bill, 1 two-dollar bill, 1 one-dollar bill, 5 half dollars, 9 quarter dollars (quarters), 4 dimes, 2 nickels, and 1 penny. However, these odd coins are always written in the decimal system. A half dollar is never written $\frac{1}{2}$ but always $0.50. In the same way a quarter is $0.25, a dime is $0.10, a nickel is $0.05, and a penny is $0.01.

(Alternatively, coins may be written in cents rather than dollars; as 1¢, 5¢, 10¢, 25¢ and 50¢, but

---

* The term "eagle" applied specifically to the $10 gold piece coined by the United States in former years. It got its name from the fact that an eagle, a familiar emblem of our country, was shown on the reverse side. (Similarly, the gold pound coined by England is popularly called a "sovereign" because the head of the English monarch appears on it.) The disappearance of gold coins from circulation in America is one of the reasons why "eagle" is now a forgotten term, but in the old days a $20 gold piece was a "double eagle," a $5 gold piece a "half eagle" and a $2.50 gold piece a "quarter eagle."

The decimal system of American coinage can be continued upward if we make use of some of the slang terms that have been applied to bills of large size. For instance ten eagles equal a "C-note" ($100 bill) and ten "C-notes" equal a "grand" ($1000 bill).

the decimal system is maintained.)

We are so used to this that we never think of the convenience of it. Think of the British system of coinage, however, in which 4 farthings make a penny, 12 pence make a shilling and 20 shillings make a pound. An Englishman, trying to add 4 pounds, 8 shillings, 2 pence, and 15 pounds, 19 shillings, 11 pence has a hard job, rather. (The answer is 20 pounds, 8 shillings, 1 penny, but I'll leave it to you to figure out how it was done.)

In fact, the British youngster spends considerable time learning how to add sums of money and how to make change, whereas the American youngster needn't. As soon as he learns arithmetic, he can handle the American coin system.

However, the United States holds the messy end of the stick, along with Great Britain, when it comes to ordinary measures. The standard system of measures used throughout the civilized world, *except* in the English-speaking countries, is the "metric system" which was invented in France in 1791.

The metric system is decimal. To take an example, we can consider units of length. The metric unit of length is the "meter" (which is 39.37 inches in length, and from which the system gets its name). Ten meters is a "dekameter," ten dekameters is a "hectometer," and ten hectometers is a "kilometer." Working it the other way, a tenth of a meter is a "decimeter" and a tenth of that is a "centimeter" and a tenth of that is a "millimeter."*

This means that something which is 2 kilometers, 5 hectometers, 1 dekameter, 7 meters, 8 decimeters, 2 centimeters, 9 millimeters long is 2517.829 meters long. You run it together as simply as that. If you have two objects, one of which is 2 meters, 8 decimeters, 9 centimeters long and the other 5 meters, 5 decimeters, 5 centimeters long, the combined length is 2.89 + 5.55 or 8.44 meters, which can also be read 8 meters, 4 decimeters, 4 centimeters (or 8 meters and 44 centimeters, if you choose).

Compare this with the English and American system of measuring length. Start with the inch. To begin with, 12 inches are a foot; 3 feet are a yard; $5 \frac{1}{2}$ yards are a rod; 40 rods are a furlong;

---

* The word "meter" (*mètre*, in French) comes from the Latin word "metrum," meaning "to measure." The prefixes for the multiples of the meter come from Greek words while those for the subdivisions of the meter come from Latin words. Thus, the prefixes "deka-," "hecto-" and "kilo-" come from the Greek words "deka" (ten), "hekaton" (hundred) and "chilioi" (thousand). The prefixes "deci-," "centi-" and "milli-" come from the Latin words "decem" (ten), "centum" (hundred) and "mille" (thousand).

and 8 furlongs are a mile. Obviously, this is too complicated so rods and furlongs are practically never used. Instead, it is taken that 1760 yards $\left(5\frac{1}{2} \times 40 \times 8\right)$ make a mile.

Even so, how much is 1 mile, 1632 yards plus 2 miles, 854 yards? The answer is 4 miles, 726 yards, but how did I get it and can you work out the problem yourself?

Or, if we stick to smaller units, how much is 3 yards, 2 feet, 8 inches plus 5 yards, 2 feet, 7 inches? Answer: 9 yards, 2 feet, 3 inches. How was it done?

American school children have to spend much time learning how to handle such units. They must also learn how to handle units of volume, weight, area and so on, each of which has its own variety of traditional nonsense. Generally, they never learn it thoroughly. Soviet school children, on the other hand (the Soviet Union having adopted the metric system), have no trouble. They handle all types of units by ordinary addition.

Why do we stick to our burdensome system of measures instead of adopting the decimal metric system? Partly because it would mean a large initial investment as all sorts of tools would have to be scrapped and redesigned to fit the new units. Mostly, though, it is tradition. People are used to old ways and change only reluctantly. In a case like this, they would have to be forced by the government, and Britain and America also have a tradition of not being forced to do things by the government.

American and British scientists, by the way, who value simplicity of manipulation even above the comfort of a rut, have uniformly adopted the metric system.   In fact, American scientists sometimes use the metric system almost irreverently.   For instance, scientists in government employ often have to deal with large quantities of money and a thousand dollars is sometimes jokingly referred to as a "kilobuck."   (The expression "buck," of course, is well-known slang for a dollar — perhaps because "buck" was earlier a slang term for a poker chip.) Similarly, a million dollars is referred to as a "megabuck" since the prefix "mega-" (from the Greek "megas," meaning "great") is used in the metric system to denote a million of something.

LOCATING THE DECIMAL POINT

So far, the decimal system may look like heaven on earth compared to ordinary fractions, but actually, like all heavens on earth, it has its drawbacks.   For instance, there is always the question of putting the decimal point in the right position.

As an example, consider the problem: 0.2×0.2. You might try to solve this multiplication by reasoning as follows: $2 + 2 = 4$ and $2 \times 2 = 4$; therefore since $0.2 + 0.2 = 0.4$, ought not 0.2×0.2 also equal 0.4?

Well, it ought not, and let's see why. If we switch to fractions (which we have learned to handle), the decimal 0.2 becomes $\frac{2}{10}$. Now if we multiply in that fashion, then it appears that $\frac{2}{10} \times \frac{2}{10} = \frac{4}{100}$; (numerator times numerator, denominator times denominator). And $\frac{4}{100}$ in decimals is 0.04. Consequently 0.2×0.2 is *not* 0.4; $0.2 \times 0.2 = 0.04$.

We can try other multiplications of decimals, checking the results by working with the equivalent fractions, and it will turn out, for instance, that $0.82 \times 0.21 = 0.1722$ while $0.82 \times 2.1 = 1.722$. $\left(\text{After all, } \frac{82}{100} \times \frac{21}{100} = \frac{1722}{10,000} \text{ while } \frac{82}{100} \times \frac{21}{10} = \frac{1722}{1000}.\right)$

In the end it is possible to decide upon a general rule: In multiplying decimals, the number of figures to the right of the decimal point in the answer is equal to the total number of figures to the right of the decimal points in the numbers being multiplied.

Thus 0.2 and 0.2, between them, have a total of

two figures to the right of the decimal point and so does 0.04 (you count the zero to the right of the decimal point as a figure).

Naturally, if one of the numbers being multiplied is an integer, it doesn't affect the position of the decimal point. The decimal point has the same location in the answer, then, that it has in the one number being multiplied that is a decimal. Thus, $0.2 \times 2 = 0.4$; $1.5 \times 5 = 7.5$ and $1.1 \times 154 = 169.4$. This, you see, goes along with the rule. In each case, the number of figures to the right of the decimal point in the answer is equal to the total number of figures to the right of the decimal point in the numbers being multiplied.

Working out the position of the decimal point in the division of decimals can be done similarly, though in reverse. Actually, though, it is customary to simplify the matter by removing the decimal point from the divisor (or from the denominator, when the division is written in fraction form). Suppose, for instance, that you wanted to divide 1.82 by 0.2. This can be expressed as $\frac{1.82}{0.2}$ and, as a fraction, it will retain its value if top and bottom are multiplied by 10. Now 1.82×10 (following our decimal rule) becomes 18.20 or 18.2, since the last 0 adds nothing to the numerical value and can be dropped. Similarly $0.2 \times 10 = 2.0$ and that is just

2 (since 2 plus 0 tenths is no different from saying simply 2).

Consequently the fraction can be written as $\frac{18.2}{2}$ and now the denominator is an integer. Since it is an integer, the division can be carried through without changing the position of the decimal point in the numerator (as in the similar cases mentioned in connection with multiplication). There being one figure to the right of the decimal point in the numerator, there must be one figure to the right in the quotient and $\frac{18.2}{2} = 9.1$.

This gives us a method for the conversion of ordinary fractions to decimals by division. Suppose we wanted the decimal equivalent of $\frac{1}{40}$. We could write it as $\frac{1.000}{40}$ and since we are dividing by an integer the position of the decimal point would not change. The division would proceed as follows:

$$
\begin{array}{r}
.025 \\
40\overline{\smash{\big)}\,1.000} \\
\underline{80} \\
200 \\
\underline{200} \\
0
\end{array}
$$

The decimal equivalent of $\frac{1}{40}$ is shown to be 0.025.

You can check this by converting 0.025 into ordinary fractions. It is $\frac{2}{100} + \frac{5}{1000}$, or $\frac{20}{1000} + \frac{5}{1000}$ or $\frac{25}{1000}$, and this last if divided, top and bottom, by 25, does indeed prove to be $\frac{1}{40}$.

MOVING THE DECIMAL POINT

Let's take a closer look at this business of multiplying by 10. Some paragraphs back, we multiplied 1.82 by 10 and got 18.2. Notice that the multiplication had the effect of doing nothing more than moving the decimal point one place to the right. In the same way, multiplication by 100 would have moved it two places to the right, multiplication by 1000 would have moved it three places to the right, and so on. (Try it and see.)

Conversely, division by 10 would simply involve moving the decimal point to the left. Thus 1.82 ÷ 10 would, by the rule of reciprocals, be equivalent to $1.82 \times \frac{1}{10}$. This, in decimals, would be 1.82 × 0.1 and if this were carried out with attention to the rule for locating the decimal point in multiplications, the answer would turn out to be 0.182. As you see, the decimal point is indeed moved one place to the left.

Dividing by 100 would, in the same way, move the decimal point two places to the left; dividing by 1000 would move it three steps to the left and so on.

Because changing a figure by multiplications or divisions of 10 results in keeping the numbers and just moving the decimal point, there turns out to be a particular convenience in the notion of "per cent."

It is usually the custom, you see, with those people (or institutions) who lend money in the way of business, to expect a little cash (called "interest") to be added to the loan when it is returned. This is to compensate them for the inconvenience of having to do without the money for a period of time, and also for the risk they took of not having the money returned at all. As an example, the lending person or institution might ask $6 a year interest for every $100 loaned.

Since interest is usually calculated by hundred-dollar units (that is, as so many dollars per year for every $100 loaned) and since the Latin for "by hundred" is "per centum," we get our word "per cent." This is symbolized as % (a form of the division sign, actually) and we speak of a return of $6 a year on every $100 loaned as "six per cent interest."

Generally in business, profits, markups, com-

missions, authors' royalties and other similar matters are calculated as percentage.

Now 1 per cent, meaning $1 for every $100,
represents $\dfrac{1}{100}$. Taking 1 per cent of any figure is
accomplished, therefore, simply by moving the
decimal point two places to the left. Thus, 1
per cent of $1350 is $13.50. The quantity repre-
sented by 6 per cent of $1350 would be $6 \times \dfrac{1}{100}$ or
or $6 \times \$13.50$ or $81.00.

A 10 per cent commission would be $\dfrac{10}{100}$ of the original figure, or $\dfrac{1}{10}$. In this case, the decimal point is
moved one step to the left. A 10 per cent com-
mission on $1350 would be $135.

Sometimes there's trouble. A 1 per cent commission on $675.37 would be $6.7537. As a matter
of practical business, figures more than two points
to the right of the decimal point in money (that is,
fractions of a cent) are rounded off and the commission is considered to be $6.75.

All this works nicely in decimal coinage; not so
nicely in British coinage. A 10 per cent commission on 135 pounds, 10 shillings turns out to be
13 pounds, 11 shillings. (Can you work that out?)

DECIMALS WITHOUT END

A more serious annoyance in the decimal system than the mere problem of finding the decimal point is the fact that some fractions can't be expressed as decimals in the ordinary way.

For instance, how do we write $\frac{1}{3}$ as a decimal?

To find out, we will write $\frac{1}{3}$ as $\frac{1.00000000}{3}$ and proceed to divide it as follows:

$$
\begin{array}{r}
.3333\ldots\ldots \\
3\,\overline{\smash{)}\,1.0000000000} \\
\underline{9} \\
10 \\
\underline{9} \\
10 \\
\underline{9} \\
10
\end{array}
$$

But it is no use continuing. You can see it will go on like that forever. The decimal equivalent of $\frac{1}{3}$ is 0.333333333 and so on, just as long as we care to continue it.

Take $\frac{1}{7}$ as the next example. If you convert this to $\frac{1.000000000}{7}$ and perform the division (I leave it to you), you will find the decimal equivalent of $\frac{1}{7}$ to be 0.142857142857142857142857 and so on as far as you care to work it. Notice the endless repetition of 142857 in the decimal equivalent of $\frac{1}{7}$.

There is no end to the decimal equivalent of $\frac{1}{7}$ any more than there is an end to the decimal equivalent of $\frac{1}{3}$. In the decimal equivalent of $\frac{1}{3}$, the figure 3 keeps repeating forever, while in the decimal equivalent of $\frac{1}{7}$, the group of figures 142857 keeps repeating forever.

These are examples of "repeating decimals."

In a sense, all decimals can be considered repeating decimals. Even the decimal equivalent of $\frac{1}{2}$ which comes to a neat and precise 0.5 can be regarded as being really 0.5000000000 ... with an endlessly repeated zero.

Sometimes a dot is placed over a number in a decimal to show that that number repeats. Thus $\frac{1}{3}$ can be written as $0.\dot{3}$ and $\frac{1}{2}$ can be written as $0.5\dot{0}$. If it is a group of numbers that is being repeated, that group can be enclosed in parentheses and a dot placed over it, so that $\frac{1}{7}$ can be written as $0.(14\overset{\cdot}{2}857)$.

Actually, any fraction you can possibly write will have a repeating decimal as its equivalent (even if the repeating unit is only a zero) and any repeating decimal you care to make up has some definite fraction as an equivalent.

You may wonder how to handle a repeating decimal such as 0.333333 . . . in arithmetical manipulations. One way out is to use the fraction $\frac{1}{3}$. In practical problems of science and engineering, the problem, oddly enough, does not exist, but I'll get to that later in connection with decimals that are even more annoying than these repeaters I have just discussed.

6
6
6
The Shape of Numbers
6

THE GREEK MATHEMATICIANS were essentially geometers and they spent considerable time in arranging dots into geometric shapes and counting them. For instance, dots can be arranged in triangles or squares, as shown in the accompanying figure. A number of dots which will just make a triangle, for instance, is a "triangular number."

You can imagine a single dot as forming a submicroscopic triangle all by itself. Three dots will make a triangle with two dots on a side. Six dots will make a larger one (three dots on a side); ten dots a still larger one (four dots on a side) and so on.

You can write all the triangular numbers in a line: 1, 3, 6, 10, 15, 21, 28, 36, 45, 55, and so on, each one representing a triangle with one more dot to the side than that represented by the number to the left. You can continue such a list of numbers as long as you want.

Observe that these numbers show a certain regularity. The first number is simply 1. The next

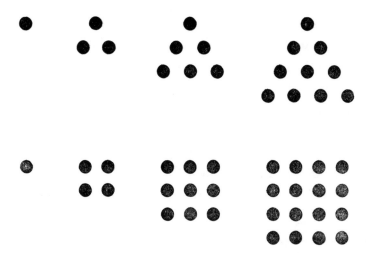

TRIANGULAR AND SQUARE NUMBERS

though is 3, which is $1 + 2$; then 6, which is $1 + 2 + 3$; then 10, which is $1 + 2 + 3 + 4$; then 15, which is $1 + 2 + 3 + 4 + 5$, and so on. Keeping this relationship in mind, you can carry on the list of triangular numbers indefinitely without ever once making a triangle and counting the dots. You can also tell if a number is a triangular number or not by trying to break it up into such a series of additions. If you succeed it's a triangular number.

Any group of numbers which can be built up successively by some scheme such as this is called a "series."

The numbers which represent the dots making up squares also form a series. Again, a single dot can be considered a submicroscopic square all by itself.

After that, though, it takes four dots to make a square with two dots on a side; nine dots to make one with three dots on a side, and so on. The series of square numbers is 1, 4, 9, 16, 25, 36, 49, 64, and so on, as long as you want to go on.

If you look at this series closely, you'll see that each number is made up of the sum of successive odd numbers. To begin with, 1 is 1; but 4 is $1 + 3$; 9 is $1 + 3 + 5$; 16 is $1 + 3 + 5 + 7$, and so on.

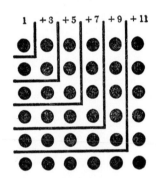

RELATIONSHIP IN TRIANGULAR AND SQUARE NUMBERS

The relationship between numbers in the triangular series and in the square series can also be shown diagrammatically, as in the accompanying figure.

The Greeks also had pentagonal numbers, as shown in the figure. These are a kind of fusion of square and triangular numbers. If you build up pentagons with dots, you will find they make a series of numbers, as follows: 1, 5, 12, 22, 35, 51, 70,

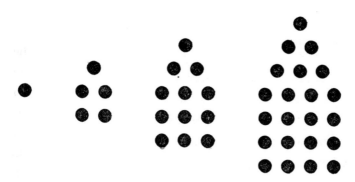

PENTAGONAL NUMBERS

and so on. These are built up by adding up numbers
at intervals of 3. Thus, 1 is 1; 5 is $1 + 4$; 12 is
$1 + 4 + 7$; 22 is $1 + 4 + 7 + 10$, and so on.

The Greeks had still other geometrical figures
which they made out of dots and, in general, the
numbers resulting from such mathematical doodling
are called "figurate numbers." Some of their
figures were solids. For instance, cubes can be
built up out of dots. Such cubes are hard to show
on paper, but if you'll look closely at the accompanying figures, you may get the idea. The series

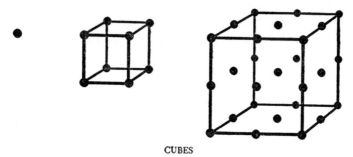

CUBES

of cubic numbers is 1, 8, 27, 64, 125, and so on.

There's a relationship here, too, that involves the addition of odd numbers as in the case of square numbers, but the addition does not start from 1 in each case. Thus 1 is 1, while 8 is 3 + 5; 27 is 7 + 9 + 11; 64 is 13 + 15 + 17 + 19, and so on. Each group of numbers being added together starts where the previous one left off and each group contains one more number than does the one before.

EXCLAMATION POINT!

So far the series of numbers I have presented can be built up by repeated additions. Multiplications, however, may also be involved. One of the kinds of series involving multiplications arises as follows:

Suppose you have 4 beads of different colors which you intend to string. How many different color patterns can you create out of those 4 beads?

If the beads are red, yellow, blue, and green (any other colors would do) you might begin by stringing any one of the four. Right there you have 4 possibilities. Having strung one, you can then string any of the remaining three, so that you have 4 × 3, or 12 possibilities so far. With two colors already strung, you can put on either one of the two remaining beads and that gives you 4 × 3 × 2, or 24 possibilities. Finally, with three beads strung there is only one left and you have $4 \times 3 \times 2 \times 1$, or 24 possibilities. The accompanying chart shows this and lists the 24 color combinations possible.

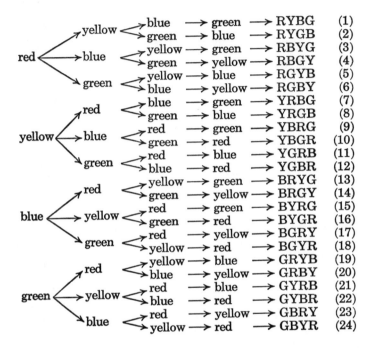

As you see, the number 24 was built up as the product of $4 \times 3 \times 2 \times 1$. By using the same kind of argument you can show that the possible combinations of 7 different beads is $7 \times 6 \times 5 \times 4 \times 3 \times 2 \times 1$, or 5040, and similarly for any number of beads.

Numbers built up by the multiplication of various

digits in succession, beginning with 1, are called "factorials." The product of $4 \times 3 \times 2 \times 1$ is called "factorial 4," 4 being the highest number involved in the multiplication. Similarly, $7 \times 6 \times 5 \times 4 \times 3 \times 2 \times 1$ is "factorial 7." Factorials are usually symbolized by use of the exclamation point. Thus "factorial 4" can be represented as 4!

The exclamation point is perhaps justified since the series increases very rapidly. The series of factorials represented by 1!, 2!, 3!, 4! and so on, is 1, 2, 6, 24, 120, 720, 5040, 40320, 362880, and on and on. The twentieth number in the series (20!) would be 2432932008176640000.

SQUARES, CUBES AND BEYOND

As a matter of fact, if we go back to the square numbers and cube numbers, we can see, easily enough, that although there is a regular relationship involving addition, there is also a regular relationship involving multiplication.

Back at the beginning of Chapter 3, I talked about the area of squares. You may remember that a square with a side equal to 1 unit (foot, inch, anything else) has an area of 1×1, or 1 square unit. A square with a side equal to 2 has an area equal to 2×2, or 4. In fact, if we consider a series of squares with sides equal to 1, 2, 3, 4, 5, 6, 7 (and so on) units, the areas in square units come out successively as 1, 4, 9, 16, 25, 36, 49, and so on.

This is, you see, the series of square numbers which I mentioned earlier in the chapter. Instead of writing that series, then, as 1, 1 + 3, 1 + 3 + 5, 1 + 3 + 5 + 7, and so on, we can write it 1 × 1, 2 × 2, 3 × 3, 4 × 4, 5 × 5, and so on.

Now a cube is a three-dimensional figure (having length, breadth, and thickness) in which all three dimensions are equal in length. A pair of dice are actually a pair of cubes. The volume of a cube is obtained by multiplying length, breadth, and thickness. This can be shown by the same type of reasoning which was used in Chapter 3 to show that the area of a square (or of any oblong) could be obtained by multiplying its length and breadth.

A cube 1 unit on each side has a volume of 1 × 1 × 1, or 1 cubic unit. A cube 2 on each side has a volume of 2 × 2 × 2, or 8. By continuing this, you will see at once that the volumes of cubes with sides of 1, 2, 3, 4, 5, 6, and so on will give the series of cubic numbers, 1, 8, 27, 64, 125, 216, and so on. These therefore can be represented as: 1 × 1 × 1; 2 × 2 × 2; 3 × 3 × 3; 4 × 4 × 4; 5 × 5 × 5; and so on.

Squares and cubes are well named but, leaving the actual geometrical figures to one side, we can imagine other series of numbers built up in which each number is the product of 4 numbers multiplied together, or 5, or 6, or any number.

Successive multiplications of the same number turn out to be endlessly useful in mathematics, and new symbols are needed. Remember that the frequent use of operations such as $6 + 6 + 6 + 6$ required the invention of the shorter and more easily grasped 6×4. In the same way, the frequent use of operations such as $6 \times 6 \times 6 \times 6$ resulted in the use of a new type of symbol, 6^4.

To begin with, 6^4 simply meant "four 6's multiplied together"; similarly 10^5 would mean "five 10's multiplied together," while 3^2 would mean "two 3's multiplied together."

The series of square numbers could be written as follows in this notation: 1^2, 2^2, 3^2, 4^2, 5^2, and so on. The series of cubes could be written: 1^3, 2^3, 3^3, 4^3, 5^3, and so on.

The small number above the line is called an "exponent" and a number containing an exponent, such as 6^4, is an "exponential number." The number being multiplied, the 6 of the 6^4, for instance, is the "base" of the exponential number.

The repeated multiplication of a number is spoken of as raising that number to a certain power. Thus, 6^4 is "six to the fourth power" or more simply, "six to the fourth." Similarly, 10^5 is "ten

to the fifth." You could, if you wished, speak of
3^2 or 3^3 as "three to the second" or "three to the
third" without actually being incorrect. However,
it is much more common to bow to the old Greek
custom and speak of those two expressions as
"three squared" and "three cubed."

AVOIDING MULTIPLICATION

The usefulness of exponential numbers lies in this:
they offer us a method for converting multiplication
into addition (and it is easier to add than to multiply).

For instance, suppose you multiplied 16 and 64.
The product is 1024. But 16 is 4×4 and 64 is
$4 \times 4 \times 4$. If we make these changes, then
16×64 becomes $4 \times 4 \times 4 \times 4 \times 4$, which is
indeed 1024, if you work it out.

Or 16 can also be considered as $2 \times 2 \times 2 \times 2$,
while 64 is $2 \times 2 \times 2 \times 2 \times 2 \times 2$. Therefore
16×64 can be expressed as $2 \times 2 \times 2 \times 2 \times 2 \times$
$2 \times 2 \times 2 \times 2 \times 2$, and this is also 1024, if you
work it out.

Using exponentials, we can consider 16 as either
4^2 or 2^4; 64 as either 4^3 or 2^6; and 1024 as either 4^5 or
2^{10}. We can write the problem $16 \times 64 = 1024$ in
either of two ways exponentially: $4^2 \times 4^3 = 4^5$ or
$2^4 \times 2^6 = 2^{10}$. Notice that in each case, the
exponent of the answer is the sum of the exponents
of the two numbers being multiplied.

If you'll try it with other numbers that can be expressed in exponential form, you'll find that this relationship will hold generally, provided that all the exponents concerned involve the same base. Thus, without going through actual multiplications, we can be assured that $2^4 \times 2^2 \times 2^{14} = 2^{20}$, and that $8^4 \times 8^7 = 8^{11}$.

This system also works for division, except that here exponents must be subtracted. Thus, $2^5 \div 2^3 = 2^2$, which, in ordinary numbers, is $32 \div 8 = 4$, and that checks, you see.

This may seem to you to be too restricted a trick to be of much use. In the first place, numbers must be capable of being expressed as exponentials. Multiplying 8 and 16 is fine since this is $2^3 \times 2^4$, but what about multiplying 7 and 17? Or even if numbers are capable of being expressed as exponentials, they may not have the same base. For instance, 8×9 is $2^3 \times 3^2$ and here you can't use the same trick of adding exponents. The answer is neither 2^5 nor 3^5; nor is it halfway between.

Why bother, then, with this? Well, any trick which will convert multiplication into addition would be so valuable that it is worth concentrating on. To make it work more generally, we must generalize the notion of exponents.

So far we have considered an exponent as representing so many of a figure multiplied together.

Under those conditions, the smallest possible exponent is 2, since you can't have less than 2 figures multiplied together. However, we can consider that that definition has now served its purpose and we can carry on beyond 2 by means of what we have now learned about exponents.

TO ZERO AND BEYOND — AGAIN

For instance, $16 \div 8 = 2$. Since $16 = 2^4$ and $8 = 2^3$, then the division may be expressed as $2^4 \div 2^3 = 2$. But if we subtract exponents, then $2^4 \div 2^3 = 2^1$. We can only decide that 2^1 and 2 are the same thing; in other words that $2^1 = 2$.

The same logic would work for exponentials involving any base, so we can set up the general rule that any number raised to the first power remains unchanged. Therefore, $5^1 = 5$; $27^1 = 27$, and so on.

But things will grow odder. For instance, what is $8 \div 8$? It is 1, obviously. But 8 is 2^3, so $2^3 \div 2^3 = 1$. Yes, of course, but by subtraction of exponents, it turns out that $2^3 \div 2^3 = 2^0$. Does this mean that $2^0 = 1$? It seems as though it must.

This may astonish you. Perhaps you can accept 2^1 being equal to 2, since, even though the phrase "one 2 multiplied together" sounds odd, you can imagine the single 2 just standing there and then it is really equal to 2. However, 2^0 seems to mean "no 2's multiplied together" and surely that can only mean that 2^0 is equal to zero. This may seem logical, certainly, but mathematics is not really concerned with everyday logic (are you shocked?) but with internal consistency.

In other words, mathematicians are willing to set up any rules, however crazy they may seem to the ordinary way of thinking, as long as those rules don't contradict one another in anything that results. The trick of adding and subtracting exponents works so well that if it ends up by showing us that 2^0 is equal to 1, we *define* it as equal to 1 and end the argument.

If, instead of $2^3 \div 2^3$, we try $6^3 \div 6^3$, we find that 6^0 is also equal to 1. In fact, if we try number after number, it should soon dawn on us that *any* number raised to the zero power is equal to 1.

Now let's go further. If we divide 64 by 128, the answer is $\frac{64}{128}$ or $\frac{1}{2}$. Exponentially, the problem is $2^6 \div 2^7$ and the answer to that is 2^{-1}. This means that 2^{-1} must equal $\frac{1}{2}$, or to put the latter in the exponential form also, $\left(\frac{1}{2}\right)^1$.

Similarly, $32 \div 128 = \left(\frac{1}{4}\right)$. Put in exponential form this is $2^5 \div 2^7 = 2^{-2}$, so that 2^{-2} must equal

$\frac{1}{4}$, which is in turn equal to $\left(\frac{1}{2}\right)^2$. If you try other examples you'll find out that, in general, a negative exponent can be turned into a positive exponent by taking the reciprocal of the number.

In other words, $4^{-7} = \left(\frac{1}{4}\right)^7$ and $10^{-3} = \left(\frac{1}{10}\right)^3$. For that matter, it works the other way around. The exponential 6^4 is equal to $\left(\frac{1}{6}\right)^{-4}$.

I can give examples now, showing that this view of exponents is consistent. For instance, is $\left(\frac{1}{6}\right)^4$ really equal to 6^{-4}? Well, let's see. The expression $\left(\frac{1}{6}\right)^4$ can be put in this form: $1 \div 6^4$. But 1 is equal to 6^0 so the expression becomes $6^0 \div 6^4$, and by subtracting exponents, the result proves indeed to be 6^{-4}.

Then again, is 6^0 really equal to 1? Well, $36 \times \frac{1}{36} = 1$, as I am sure you are willing to grant. Since $36 = 6^2$, then $\frac{1}{36} = \left(\frac{1}{6}\right)^2$ or 6^{-2}. The expression $36 \times \frac{1}{36}$ becomes, therefore, $6^2 \times 6^{-2}$, which by addition becomes 6^0 which therefore equals 1.

Of course, none of this really proves anything,

since it involves what the mathematician calls
"circular reasoning." (This is what happens when
you say: "A cat is any animal that says meow."
Then "That animal says meow so it is a cat.")
Nevertheless, it does show that the exponent system
hangs together.

We can show it in another way, too, by listing
some exponential figures. We can begin with the
old definition of numbers multiplied together,
so that:

$$2^6 = 2 \times 2 \times 2 \times 2 \times 2 \times 2 = 64$$
$$2^5 = 2 \times 2 \times 2 \times 2 \times 2 \quad\quad = 32$$
$$2^4 = 2 \times 2 \times 2 \times 2 \quad\quad\quad = 16$$
$$2^3 = 2 \times 2 \times 2 \quad\quad\quad\quad = 8$$
$$2^2 = 2 \times 2 \quad\quad\quad\quad\quad = 4$$

Now if you will ignore the number of 2's being
multiplied together and just consider the final
figures, you will notice that every time the exponent
decreases by 1, the final figure is cut in half. Let's
just continue that:

$$2^1 = 2$$
$$2^0 = 1$$
$$2^{-1} = \frac{1}{2}$$
$$2^{-2} = \frac{1}{4}$$
$$2^{-3} = \frac{1}{8}$$

If we do, you see, it turns out that the exponents less than 2 mean just what we have decided they must mean. This can be worked out for any base. You will find that exponents to the base 3 will involve values that are cut to $\frac{1}{3}$ each time the exponent is decreased by 1; exponentials with the base 6 will be cut to $\frac{1}{6}$ each time and so on. But in every case, the system will work.

All this means we have increased the chances of having multiplication changed to addition. Now we can multiply $\frac{1}{8}$ and 1024 by exponents. However, we still haven't decided how to multiply 7 and 17.

Can we then broaden exponents still further? Now that we have both positive and negative exponents, what about fractional exponents? Well, before we can consider what fractional exponents might mean, we have to consider the reverse of "raising to a power."

7
7
7
Digging for Roots
7

DESCENDING FROM A POWER

So FAR, every form of mathematical manipulation I have discussed has had its reverse. For addition there has been subtraction and for multiplication there has been division. Now that we've been considering raising to a power, it is natural to ask what the reverse of that is. Since raising to a power consists of repeated multiplication, the reverse must consist of repeated division.

For instance, 32 can be divided by 2 to give 16, which can be divided by 2 to give 8, which can be divided by 2 to give 4, which can be divided by 2 to give 2, which can be divided by 2 to give 1. In condensed form, $32 \div 2 \div 2 \div 2 \div 2 \div 2 = 1$. (As in division, which I discussed in Chapter 3, the trick is to end at one exactly.) Since this division by 2 was repeated 5 times in reducing 32 to 1, 2 can be spoken of as the "fifth root of 32."

Again $81 \div 3 \div 3 \div 3 \div 3 = 1$, so 3 is the "fourth root of 81." (Why "root"? Well, 32 grows out of a foundation of 2's and 81 out of a foundation of 3's as a plant grows out of a foundation of roots.)

The symbol for a root is $\sqrt{}$. The variety of the root is indicated by a small number in the upper left. Thus, the fifth root of 32 is written $\sqrt[5]{32}$, and the fourth root of 81 is written $\sqrt[4]{81}$. The sign $\sqrt{}$ is called the "radical sign" and numbers containing roots are called "radicals," this word coming from a Latin word, "radix," meaning "root."

These higher roots are met with only on occasion. By far the most common type of root is the one that is the reverse of the square. In other words 25 is the square of 5, and therefore 5 is the $\sqrt[2]{25}$. Strictly speaking, $\sqrt[2]{25}$ should be called the "second root of 25" since $25 \div 5 \div 5 = 1$. However, the familiarity of the term "square" overpowered consistency. The "second root of a square number" became shortened to "square root" and this has been universally adopted. The "second root of 25" is always spoken of as the "square root of 25." (Similarly, "third roots" are called "cube roots.")

The square root is so familar that it is even universally customary to leave out the little 2 and write the square root of 25, for instance, as simply $\sqrt{25}$.

The next question to arise, though, is how one goes about determining what the root of a number is. So far I have been working backwards. I happen to know that 2^5 is 32, so I know that if I divide 32 by 2 five times, I will arrive at 1. (After all, having raised a number to a power, it is simple to reverse my steps and descend from the power once more.)

Actually, the method for determining roots arithmetically makes use of this "working backwards" deal, even more so than does long division. For instance, working out the square root of 625 looks like this:

$$\begin{array}{r} 25 \\ \sqrt{625} \\ 4 \end{array}$$

$$45\overline{)\begin{array}{r}225\\225\\\hline 0\end{array}}$$

You put down the first 2 of the answer by working backward and knowing that 2×2 is 4 which is as close as you can get to 6. If you try 3, you reach $3 \times 3 = 9$ and have shot past the mark. You must then subtract and carry down two figures instead of the usual one figure in long division, which this seems to resemble a bit. (If you were working cube roots, you would have to carry down three figures; with fourth roots four figures, and so on.) To get the next figure, you have to divide 225 by 45. You arrive at 45 by doubling the first figure of your answer, which gives you the 4. The second figure must be the same as the second figure in your answer and you have to try various figures to see which will give the closest number to 225. The figure 5 does it since $5 \times 45 = 225$ exactly.

This may strike you as awfully complicated and it is, there's no denying it, but the process gives rise to some vital results.

For instance, what is the square root of 2, or, in symbols, $\sqrt{2}$? What number multiplied by itself gives 2 as an answer?

To begin with, we can see at once that no integer will serve as the answer, for $1 \times 1 = 1$ and $2 \times 2 = 4$. The first is too small and the latter too large. The answer must lie between 1 and 2 and, therefore, be a fraction.

Can we speak of a fractional square root? Why not? By our original definition of exponential figures, $\left(1 \frac{2}{5}\right)^2$ would mean $1 \frac{2}{5} \times 1 \frac{2}{5}$ and the answer to that is $1 \frac{24}{25}$, if you care to work it out. That means that $\sqrt{1 \frac{24}{25}} = 1 \frac{2}{5}$. Not only have we a fractional square root, but we have a fraction in the role of a square number and both fit into the rules that hold for integers.

And, incidentally, $1 \frac{2}{5}$ multiplied by itself gives a number that is fairly close to 2, so $1 \frac{2}{5}$ must be fairly close to $\sqrt{2}$. We're only $\frac{1}{25}$ short of the goal since

the square of $1\frac{2}{5}$ is $1\frac{24}{25}$ instead of $1\frac{25}{25}$, which

would be 2.

We can cut things finer than that. The fraction

$1\frac{41}{100}$, if multiplied by itself, gives the answer

$1\frac{9881}{10000}$, which is even closer to 2. It would cer-

tainly appear that if we adjust things finely enough,

we will eventually get a fraction (perhaps a com-

plicated one) which will be exactly the square root

of 2.

But will we?

COMPARING LINES

This problem of finding the square root of 2 came

up first with the Greeks. They were geometers

primarily, as I said before, and they were very

interested in comparing the lengths of lines in

figures. For instance, suppose we consider an

oblong within which is drawn one diagonal, as

shown here. How would the length of the diagonal

compare with the length of the sides of the oblong?

The diagonal is obviously longer than either side,

but how much longer? The Greeks wanted to know.

Now when we compare the lengths of two lines,

one of which is 2 inches long and the other 1 inch
long, we say that "the lengths are as 2 is to 1."
If one is 4 inches long and the other 2 inches, we
can say that "the lengths are as 4 is to 2."

In both cases, however, the longer line is just
twice the length of the shorter. To the mathematician the fact that one line is twice as long as
the other is more interesting and significant than
the fact that one line is 2 inches and the other 4, or
that one line is 24 inches and the other 48, for that

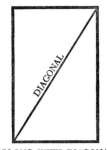

OBLONG WITH DIAGONAL

matter. He prefers, in all such cases, to say "the
lengths are as 2 is to 1."

The best way to take care of this automatically
is to represent the length comparison as a fraction.
In other words if one line is 2 inches long and the
other is 1 inch long, we can say the lengths are
$\frac{2}{1}$. Then, if our lines are 48 inches long and 24 inches
long, the fraction becomes $\frac{48}{24}$ which, as a fraction,

can be changed by dividing top and bottom by 24, becoming $\frac{2}{1}$.

A fraction representing a comparison of two similar measures (the lengths of two lines, the volumes of two pots, the weights of two men) is called a "ratio."

Of course, two lengths may not be so related as to give a simple ratio, such as 2 to 1. Suppose one line is 1 inch long and the other is 1 9/10 inches long. The ratio is not quite 2/1. It is $\frac{1\frac{9}{10}}{1}$. Fractions within fractions are, however, an unnecessary complication, which can be removed in this case by multiplying the fraction top and bottom by 10. We then end up with the ratio $\frac{19}{10}$.

Any two numbers that are expressed as fractions can be converted to a whole number ratio in this way. For instance if one line is $2\frac{4}{17}$ inches long and another is $1\frac{13}{15}$ inches long, the ratio of the two lengths would be $\frac{2\frac{4}{17}}{1\frac{13}{15}}$. If we multiply this complicated-looking fraction, top and bottom, by $127\frac{1}{2}$, the ratio becomes $\frac{285}{238}$, with only integers involved.

(This would all be much simpler using a decimal notation, but the Greeks didn't have one and the story is more dramatic if we follow it as the Greeks worked it out.)

Now we're ready to go back to our oblong, where we have our Greeks trying to discover the ratio of the lengths of the diagonal and those of the sides. To simplify matters, since the two parts of the oblong on either side of the diagonal are perfectly

RIGHT TRIANGLE WITH HYPOTENUSE

symmetrical, we can leave out one half. What is left, as in the figure, is called a "right triangle" and what was the diagonal is now called the "hypotenuse."

The Egyptians had known for many centuries, simply by actual experience, that if one side of a right triangle was 3 units long and the other side was 4 units long, the hypotenuse was just 5 units long. In such a case, the ratio of hypotenuse to the longer side was $\frac{5}{4}$ and to the shorter side $\frac{5}{3}$.

The Greeks were more general. They wanted to know the ratio for any right triangle; one in which the sides were 8 and 23 units long, or 1 and 7, or 28377 and 309621 — anything. According to the story, the Greek mathematician Pythagoras discovered that in *any* right triangle, the square of one side plus the square of the other side equaled the square of the hypotenuse. This is called the Pythagorean Theorem in his honor, although actually the Chinese seem to have known of it about 600 years before the time of Pythagoras.

Here's the way the Pythagorean Theorem works. Suppose a right triangle has one side 3 units long

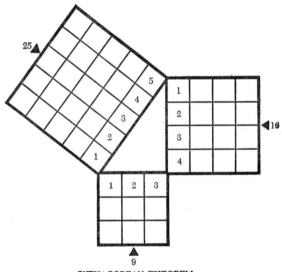

PYTHAGOREAN THEOREM

and the other 4 units long. The square of the first side is 3 × 3, or 9; the square of the second side is 4 × 4, or 16. The square of the hypotenuse is the sum of the squares of the sides, or 9 + 16 = 25. If the square of the hypotenuse is 25, then the hypotenuse itself has a length equal to the square root of 25 which, of course, is 5.

Here's another case. One side of a right triangle is 5 and the other 12. The square of the first is 5 × 5, or 25, and of the second 12 × 12, or 144. Add 25 and 144 and the sum, 169, is the square of the hypotenuse. The length of the hypotenuse is therefore $\sqrt{169}$ or 13, since 13 × 13 = 169. In this triangle, the ratio of the hypotenuse to the longer side is $\frac{13}{12}$ and to the shorter side is $\frac{13}{5}$.

Using the Pythagorean Theorem, it would certainly appear that the ratio of hypotenuse and sides could be worked out for *any* right triangle, and thus the Greek mathematicians could attain true happiness. Most of all, it should certainly work for the simplest right triangle of all, one in which both sides are equal in length (an "isosceles right triangle").

Such a triangle is shown in the figure on the following page. To make it as simple as possible, let's suppose that each side is 1 unit in length. The square of each side is 1 × 1, or 1. Summing the

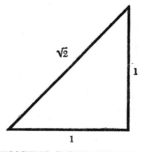

ISOSCELES RIGHT TRIANGLE

two squares, we have 2 as the square of the hypotenuse. The length of the hypotenuse would then be
$\sqrt{2}$, whatever that is.

All the Greeks had to do now was to get a fraction
which would represent $\sqrt{2}$, and then they would be
able to say that the ratio of hypotenuse to side in an
isosceles right triangle was that fraction to one.
And by suitable adjustment, they could convert
that ratio to one involving integers only — and
then they could go off and celebrate.

THE NONEXISTENCE OF FRACTIONS

Earlier in the chapter, I said that $1\frac{2}{5}$ was nearly

right as the value of $\sqrt{2}$. If it were exactly right,

the ratio would be $\frac{1\frac{2}{5}}{1}$, which could be converted to

whole numbers by multiplying top and bottom by

5, so that the ratio becomes $\frac{7}{5}$.

But, alas, $1\frac{2}{5}$ is not exactly right. The fraction

$1\frac{41}{100}$ is closer and that would give a ratio of

$\frac{1\frac{41}{100}}{1}$, or $\frac{141}{100}$ in whole numbers. The fraction $1\frac{207}{500}$

is still closer and that would give a ratio of $\frac{1\frac{207}{500}}{1}$ or

$\frac{707}{500}$ in whole numbers.

But $1\frac{207}{500}$ is not quite exactly right either. For a while, the Greek mathematicians spent their time trying to find the exact fraction that would represent $\sqrt{2}$, so that they could put the ratio $\frac{\sqrt{2}}{1}$ into whole numbers. They kept getting closer, but they never quite got the exact fraction.

Finally, the Greek mathematician Euclid proved that no matter how complicated you were willing to make the fraction, it was useless. No such fraction existed. (It is reported that Pythagoras had discovered this first but was so shocked at such an extraordinary fact that he swore his students to secrecy and kept deathly quiet about it. This story is probably untrue.)

If $\frac{\sqrt{2}}{1}$ cannot be expressed as a ratio involving integers only, then neither can any other fraction

containing $\sqrt{2}$, such as $\dfrac{\sqrt{2}}{2}$ or $\dfrac{4}{\sqrt{2}}$, since all such

fractions can be converted into $\dfrac{\sqrt{2}}{1}$ multiplied by

something. For instance $\dfrac{\sqrt{2}}{2} = \dfrac{\sqrt{2}}{1} \times \dfrac{1}{2}$. Again,

$\dfrac{\sqrt{2}}{1} \times 2 = \dfrac{2\sqrt{2}}{1}$ or, if you multiply top and bottom

by $\sqrt{2}$, it equals $\dfrac{4}{\sqrt{2}}$. (You must remember that

$\sqrt{2}$ — whatever it is — multiplied by $\sqrt{2}$ equals 2.)

Since $\sqrt{2}$ can never form part of a ratio that can be expressed in integers only, it is an "irrational number." Numbers, on the other hand, which can form part of a ratio which can be expressed in integers only are "rational numbers." All integers and fractions, positive or negative, are rational numbers.

It turns out that almost all square roots are irrational. In fact, the only numbers that have rational square roots are the integers making up the series of squares mentioned at the beginning of Chapter 6 (called the "perfect squares" because the square roots come out as exact integers), or fractions

composed of those numbers. For instance $\sqrt{1\dfrac{7}{9}}$ is a rational number, because $1\frac{7}{9} = \frac{16}{9}$, which is a fraction composed of perfect squares. The square root of $1\frac{7}{9}$ is therefore $\frac{4}{3}$ (4 being the square root of 16 and 3 being the square root of 9), or $1\frac{1}{3}$.

The fact that most square roots are irrational does not make them useless by any means. It is often necessary to use $\sqrt{2}$ in some formula that comes up in science or engineering. Its value can be worked out, by the method described earlier in the chapter, to as many decimal places as you have patience for.

For instance, $\sqrt{2}$ can be worked out to six decimal places and found to be equal to 1.414214. This is not very far from the true value since 1.414214 $\times$ 1.414214 = 2.000001237796. This answer differs from 2 by being only a trifle over one-millionth too high. For that reason 1.414214 is a good enough value for almost any practical problem involving $\sqrt{2}$. And even if it isn't, a little extra trouble will give you more decimal places — as many as you want, in fact.

However, if you want to be stubborn and insist on working out the square root ("extracting the root," it is called) until you run out of decimals, you will find that you never will. There is no end. No matter how many decimal places you work out for the square root of 2, there are more to follow.

This may strike you as the same situation which occurred in the decimal version of $\frac{1}{3}$ which is 0.333333333 . . . and so on without end, or the decimal version of $\frac{1}{7}$, which is 0.142857142857142857 . . . and so on without end, but it is not quite.

Those endless decimals have a fractional equivalent, while the decimal representing $\sqrt{2}$ does *not* have a fractional equivalent. Why not? Well, the decimal equivalents of $\frac{1}{3}$ and $\frac{1}{7}$, and of an indefinite number of other fractions of the same sort, are *repeating* decimals. Endless decimals can be converted into fractions *only* if they are repeating decimals.

The point is that the decimal one works out for $\sqrt{2}$ is *nonrepeating*. No matter how far you go, no pattern shows up, either in $\sqrt{2}$ or the decimal equivalent of any irrational number. If there were any pattern, however slight, a fraction could be made out of the decimal. If there were a million nonrepeating, patternless digits and then that whole million were repeated, over and over, a fraction could be made out of it. Or if there were a million nonrepeating digits (or a billion or a trillion) and then suddenly an endless series of . . . 555555555 . . .

or any other kind of pattern, then a fraction could be made out of it.

However, in irrational numbers, the decimal equivalents are completely nonrepeating and not the slightest pattern ever shows up or ever can show up.

(Of course you might ask how anyone can know what happens after the trillionth decimal place since no one has ever looked. Well, the pattern-lessness of the irrational decimals has been deduced, in the long run, from certain basic premises of mathematics. If a pattern were to appear in such decimals, even the slightest pattern, the entire mathematical structure would have to be revised. This is not expected to happen.)

THE EXISTENCE OF FRACTIONS

Now let's consider an expression like $(2^4)^2$. This means that the expression 2^4 is to be squared. The value of 2^4 is $2 \times 2 \times 2 \times 2$, or 16. The square of 16 is 16×16, or 256, so $(2^4)^2 = 256$. But 256 is also $2 \times 2 \times 2 \times 2 \times 2 \times 2 \times 2 \times 2$, or 2^8. Therefore $(2^4)^2 = 2^8$.

If you try this sort of thing a few more times for different bases and exponents, it will seem, in general, that in raising an exponential number to a certain power, the answer will involve multiplying the two exponents. Thus, without doing any calculating, we can know that $(3^5)^2 = 3^{10}$ and $(7^8)^7 = 7^{56}$.

If this is so, why can't we imagine a number that can be represented as, let us say, $(2^4)^{\frac{1}{2}}$? Following the system of multiplying exponents under such conditions, it would seem that $(2^4)^{\frac{1}{2}}$ is equal to 2^2. If so, since $2^4 = 16$ and $2^2 = 4$, what we are saying is that $16^{\frac{1}{2}} = 4$. But we know that the square root of 16 is 4. It would seem then that an exponent of $\frac{1}{2}$ is equivalent to taking the square root. In other words $16^{\frac{1}{2}} = \sqrt{16}$.

Furthermore, by following the same line of reasoning, $16^{\frac{1}{3}}$ can be shown to be equal to $\sqrt[3]{16}$ (that is, the cube root of 16); $16^{\frac{1}{4}}$ to the $\sqrt[4]{16}$, and so on. Here we have the introduction of fractional exponents which I promised at the end of Chapter 6. Notice also, as a curiosity, that $\sqrt{2}$, which cannot be expressed as a fraction, can be expressed by a very simple number that includes a fractional exponent; to wit, $2^{\frac{1}{2}}$.

It is even possible to get meaning out of a number like $16^{\frac{3}{2}}$ in the following manner. The number $16^{\frac{3}{2}}$ can be converted to $(16^3)^{\frac{1}{2}}$, since $3 \times \frac{1}{2} = \frac{3}{2}$. Therefore $16^{\frac{3}{2}}$, being equal to $(16^3)^{\frac{1}{2}}$, is equal to the $\sqrt{16^3}$. In general, any fractional exponent raises the base to the power indicated by the numerator and takes the root to the number indicated by the denominator.

Thus, $2^{\frac{567}{235}}$ would be the 235th root of the 567th power of 2, which could be symbolized as $\sqrt[235]{2^{567}}$.

Naturally, such fractional exponents are unwieldy. However, why not use decimals? After all, $\dfrac{1}{2}$ is equal to 0.5 so, instead of saying $4^{\frac{1}{2}}$, let's say $4^{0.5}$ power. Either way, it signifies the square root of 4, or 2.

Significance can be attached to any decimal exponent. For instance, $2^{5.175}$ is the same as saying $2^{\frac{207}{40}}$ since 5.175 is equal to $\dfrac{207}{40}$. In turn, $2^{\frac{207}{40}}$ is a number obtained by raising 2 to the 207th power and taking the 40th root of the result. (Or taking the 40th root of 2 and raising the result to the 207th power. The order of performing the two operations makes no difference. You can see that for yourself if you try it on $4^{\frac{3}{2}}$. The square root of 4^3 equals $\sqrt{64}$, which is 8. The cube of $\sqrt{4}$ is 2^3, which is also 8.)

The value of $2^{\frac{207}{40}}$ (or that of any base raised to any power, whole, fractional, or decimal, positive or negative) can be worked out approximately by the use of appropriate mathematical techniques. These do not actually involve multiplying two hundred and seven 2's or finding a fortieth root of anything. The value comes out to about 36.126.

This value is approximate because $2^{\frac{2 \cdot 0 \cdot 7}{4 \cdot 0}}$ is irrational (as is almost any number involving a fractional or decimal exponent). The decimal equivalent is therefore endless and nonrepeating, but as many places as are needed for usefulness can be worked out.

Using any number as base, then, we can express any other number in exponential form. For instance, I set myself the problem of 7×17 at the end of Chapter 6. Well, 7 can be expressed as $2^{2.81}$ or $3^{1.77}$ or $5^{1.21}$ (there being ways of calculating these exponential equivalents) while 17 is $2^{4.08}$ or $3^{2.58}$ or $5^{1.76}$.

The problem of 7×17 can then be expressed as $2^{2.81} \times 2^{4.08} = 2^{6.89}$; or $3^{1.77} \times 3^{2.58} = 3^{4.35}$; or $5^{1.21} \times 5^{1.76} = 5^{2.97}$. The numbers $2^{6.89}$, $3^{4.35}$ and $5^{2.97}$ are all about equal and all equal about 119, which is the answer.

Of course, it looks simpler to multiply 7×17 to begin with than to labor to find the exponential equivalents in decimals (which are only approximate anyway — notice that the results equal *about* 119). However, let's go on and see where we end. For one thing, in choosing a base, why choose 2 or 3 or 5? Why not choose 10, which is the key number in our number system?

8
8
8
The Very Large and Very Small
8

A NEW CONVENIENCE OF TEN

ONE OF THE REASONS WHY the use of exponentials was forced on scientists is that they found it so often necessary to work with very large and very small numbers. The mass of the earth is about 6000000000000000000000000000 grams. On the other hand, the mass of the hydrogen atom is about 0.00000000000000000000000166 grams.

As you see, it is very easy to get lost in the zeros. In trying to find their way, scientists make use of a way of expressing numbers that is partly ordinary and partly exponential. And the exponential part involves the base 10 (something at which I hinted at the end of the preceding chapter).

The powers of 10 offer an easy way to express large or small numbers in a manner that just suits our ten-based number system. You can see this in the following table, which you can check for yourself by conducting the proper multiplications:

$$1000000 = 10^6$$
$$100000 = 10^5 \qquad\qquad 0.1 = 10^{-1}$$
$$10000 = 10^4 \qquad\qquad 0.01 = 10^{-2}$$
$$1000 = 10^3 \qquad\qquad 0.001 = 10^{-3}$$
$$100 = 10^2 \qquad\qquad 0.0001 = 10^{-4}$$
$$10 = 10^1 \qquad\qquad 0.00001 = 10^{-5}$$
$$1 = 10^0 \qquad\qquad 0.000001 = 10^{-6}$$

Of course, such a table can be extended as far upward and as far downward as we like.

To demonstrate how the base 10 fits into our number system, consider the number 4372.654. We have broken this up into 4 "thousands," 3 "hundreds," 7 "tens," 2 "ones," 6 "tenths," 5 "hundredths," and 4 "thousandths." Or we could write it as $4000 + 300 + 70 + 2 + 0.6 + 0.05 + 0.004$.

However, if we use the powers of 10, remembering that 1000 is 10^3, 100 is 10^2 and so on, we can write 4372.654 as: $(4 \times 10^3) + (3 \times 10^2) + (7 \times 10^1) + (2 \times 10^0) + (6 \times 10^{-1}) + (5 \times 10^{-2}) + (4 \times 10^{-3})$.

This actually puts on paper exactly what the abacus has been doing for thousands of years. If the "ones" rung of an abacus is labeled "zero" and those above it are labeled 1, 2, 3, and so on, while those below are labeled -1, -2, -3, they are really being labeled by the power of ten which that rung represents.

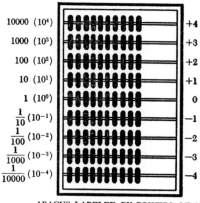

10000 (10^4)		+4
1000 (10^3)		+3
100 (10^2)		+2
10 (10^1)		+1
1 (10^0)		0
$\frac{1}{10}$ (10^{-1})		−1
$\frac{1}{100}$ (10^{-2})		−2
$\frac{1}{1000}$ (10^{-3})		−3
$\frac{1}{10000}$ (10^{-4})		−4

ABACUS LABELED BY POWERS OF 10

All the arithmetic we learn, using Arabic numbers, can be explained by studying the behavior of these powers, though this is never done in grade school.

But we will spend time on such exponentials now and see what benefits they offer.

First consider the positive powers of 10. Notice that in them the exponent is equal to the number of zeros in the ordinary number. Thus, the number of zeros in 1000000 is 6 and the exponential form is, therefore, 10^6.

Now in order to convert a number made up of digits other than 1 and 0 into an exponential with a base of 10, it is simplest to convert that number into an expression that includes an even power of 10. For instance, the mass of the earth can be written as $6 \times 1000000000000000000000000000$ grams. The

large number is now an exact power of 10, since it
consists of a 1 followed by a number of zeros, as
is true of all powers of 10. Since the number of
zeros in this particular large power is 27, it can be
expressed exponentially as 10^{27}. The mass of the
earth is 6 times this number, or 6×10^{27} grams.

There are two obvious advantages to this exponential form of a large number. First, it takes
up less room. Second, it is clearer, since we don't
have to count zeros each time we come across it.

The very small numbers involve the negative
powers of 10. These negative powers, as you see in
the table above, form ordinary numbers consisting
of a series of zeros to the right of the decimal point
ended by a 1. The numerical value of the negative
exponent is equal to one more than the number of
zeros to the right of the decimal point. For instance,
the number 0.000001 has five zeros to the right of
the decimal point and, exponentially, it is 10^{-6}.

The mass of the hydrogen atom can be expressed
as $1.66 \times 0.00000000000000000000001$.   (If you
perform the multiplication you will, indeed, get the
number originally given.) The small number is a
power of 10, being made up of zeros and a 1. It has
23 zeros to the right of the decimal point so it is
10^{-24}. The mass of the hydrogen atom is 1.66 times
this and therefore can be represented as $1.66 \times$
10^{-24} grams.

OTHER THAN TEN

Once we start putting our ten-based number system into exponential form, it becomes easy to understand a system based on some other number. For instance, I mentioned earlier in the book the convenience of using 12 instead of 10 as a base, because 12 has more factors than 10 does.*

To use 12 as a base, we would need twelve separate digits (including zero). These would be 0, 1, 2, 3, 4, 5, 6, 7, 8, 9, @, and #. I am using the symbols @ and # to represent the numbers which, in the ten-based system, are represented as 10 and 11.

Now a number like 222 in the ten-based system is $(2 \times 10^2) + (2 \times 10^1) + (2 \times 10^0)$. The same number in the twelve-based system could be converted into the ten-based system by writing it,

---

* Twelve had other advantages, in addition to the number of its factors. Ancient man told time by the moon. Every 29 or 30 days there was a new moon and, consequently, a new "month." It turned out that there were just about 12 such months (actually 12 months and $11\frac{1}{4}$ days) in the cycle of seasons — that is, in the time from spring to spring. That gave the number 12 a kind of magical value. It became important to early man. Because of this, he worked out 12 signs of the zodiac, with the sun spending one month in each sign, during its apparent circling of the earth. The twelve signs of the zodiac were probably reflected in such more earthly things as the twelve tribes of Israel and the twelve apostles.

analogously, as $(2 \times 12^2) + (2 \times 12^1) + (2 \times 12^0)$. This comes to $288 + 24 + 2$, or 314. In other words, 222 in the twelve-based system (duodecimal) is equal to 314 in the ten-based system (decimal).

You might also have a number like $3 \# 4$ in the twelve-based system. This would be equivalent to $(3 \times 12^2) + (\# \times 12^1) + (4 \times 12^0)$. Since I have set $\#$ equal to 11 in the ten-based system, this expression comes out to $432 + 132 + 4$, or 568, in that system.

You could also use a number less than 10 on which to base your system — 7 perhaps. Then you would only need 7 symbols: 0, 1, 2, 3, 4, 5, and 6. The number 435 in the seven-based system can be translated into $(4 \times 7^2) + (3 \times 7^1) + (5 \times 7^0)$, which comes out to $196 + 21 + 5$, or 222, in the ten-based system.

In this fashion the symbol for a number in any system can be converted to the equivalent symbol for that number in any other system. Even decimals can be handled. The expression 0.15 in the twelve-based system can be represented as $(1 \times 12^{-1}) + (5 \times 12^{-2})$, or $\frac{1}{12} + \frac{5}{144}$, which comes to $\frac{17}{144}$ in the ten-based system. In the seven-based system, the same expression would be $(1 \times 7^{-1}) + (5 \times 7^{-2})$, or $\frac{1}{7} + \frac{5}{49}$, which comes to $\frac{12}{49}$ in the ten-based system.

How can we tell, though, how many separate symbols are needed for any particular system? Well, the first number which requires two symbols is 10 (in any system). All numbers smaller than 10 require a separate and different symbol. All numbers over 10 can be made up of combinations of the symbols of numbers under 10. This is certainly true of the ten-based system with which we are familiar and other systems can be expected to behave similarly (and, when examined, are actually found to behave in this manner).

Well, then, what is the meaning of the expression 10 in the twelve-based system, for instance? It is $(1 \times 12^1) + (0 \times 12^0)$, or $12 + 0$, or 12, in the ten-based system. Similarly, in the seven-based system, the expression 10 is $(1 \times 7^1) + (0 \times 7^0)$ or $7 + 0$, or 7. If you check the matter for other systems, you will soon convince yourself that in a system based on a particular number, the expression 10 is equal to that number. (In the ten-based system, 10 is equal to 10, naturally.)

In the twelve-based system, then, we need separate digits for every number below 12. This means 12 separate digits, including zero. In the seven-based system, we need separate digits for every number below 7, or 7 separate digits, including zero. This would work similarly for any other system. A system based on the number 28 would require 28 separate digits, including zero.

To give you a closer look at what this means, here are the symbols for the first thirty numbers of the twelve-based system, the seven-based system and our own familiar ten-based system.

COUNTING IN ONES AND ZEROS

For each system based on a particular number,

seven-based system	ten-based system	twelve-based system
1	1	1
2	2	2
3	3	3
4	4	4
5	5	5
6	6	6
10	7	7
11	8	8
12	9	9
13	10	@
14	11	#
15	12	10
16	13	11
20	14	12
21	15	13

tables for addition, multiplication and other manipulations can be set up. In the twelve-based
system $5 + 8 = 11$ and $3 \times 4 = 10$. In the seven-
based system $3 + 6 = 12$ while $5 \times 3 = 21$. This
may look odd to us because we're not used to such
systems. However, if we were to stay within one or
another system, we would find it would suit our
purposes just as well. We've actually picked the

seven-based system	ten-based system	twelve-based system
22	16	14
23	17	15
24	18	16
25	19	17
26	20	18
30	21	19
31	22	1@
32	23	1#
33	24	20
34	25	21
35	26	22
36	27	23
40	28	24
41	29	25
42	30	26

ten-based system because we have ten fingers, not because there's anything more logical about it than about any other.

However, for a particular purpose, a particular system may turn out to be more *useful* than another, even if not more logical. This is true, for instance, of the binary system, which is a two-based system.

In a two-based system, the expression 10 is equal to 2 in the ten-based system. Consequently, there are only two digits in such a system, 0 and 1. The symbols for the first 30 numbers in such a system are listed here together with the equivalents in the ten-based system:

two-based system	ten-based system	two-based system	ten-based system
1	1	1001	9
10	2	1010	10
11	3	1011	11
100	4	1100	12
101	5	1101	13
110	6	1110	14
111	7	1111	15
1000	8	10000	16

To convert a two-based expression into the equivalent expression in the ten-based system is simple enough. Consider the binary expression 11001, for instance. This is equivalent to: $(1 \times 2^4) + (1 \times 2^3) + (0 \times 2^2) + (0 \times 2^1) + (1 \times 2^0)$, or $16 + 8 + 0 + 0 + 1$, or 25, which is actually the equivalent shown in the table.

This process can be simplified by noting that the powers of 2 are multiplied by either 0 or 1. There are no other digits in the two-based system to use. If the power is multiplied by 0, it is zero and can be ignored in the summing up. If it is multiplied by 1, it is the power itself.

two-based system	ten-based system	two-based system	ten-based system
10001	17	11000	24
10010	18	11001	25
10011	19	11010	26
10100	20	11011	27
10101	21	11100	28
10110	22	11101	29
10111	23	11110	30

Therefore we can count the places in a number like 11001 from right to left, starting with zero, thus: $1\ 1\ 0\ 0\ 1$. Each small number represents the particular power of 2 represented by that position in the number. Only those powers in which a 1 appears need be considered. Using that system, 11001 is $2^4 + 2^3 + 2^0$, or $16 + 8 + 1$, or 25.

A larger number such as $1\ 1\ 1\ 0\ 0\ 1\ 0\ 1\ 0\ 0\ 0\ 0\ 1\ 0\ 0\ 1$ can be translated in the same way. Since there are 1's in positions 0, 3, 8, 10, 13, 14, and 15, the numbers represent $2^{15} + 2^{14} + 2^{13} + 2^{10} + 2^8 + 2^3 + 2^0$, or $32{,}768 + 16{,}384 + 8{,}192 + 1{,}024 + 256 + 8 + 1$, or 58,633.

Translating the other way is more tedious but not very difficult. Suppose we considered the expressed 1562 in the ten-based system. It can be translated into the binary system as follows:

The largest power of 2 which is smaller than 1562 is 2^{10} (which is 1024). If that is subtracted from 1562, it leaves 538. The largest power of 2 smaller than that is 2^9 (which is 512 and leaves 26). Then we have 2^4 (which is 16 and leaves 10), 2^3 (which is 8 and leaves 2) and 2^1 (which is 2 and leaves nothing). In powers of 2, then, $1562 = 2^{10} + 2^9 + 2^4 + 2^3 + 2^1$.

Now it is only necessary to count off spaces from right to left, starting from zero. We place 1's in positions 1, 3, 4, 9, and 10 (corresponding to the powers of 2 that make up the number) and 0's elsewhere. Doing this, we have 11000011010. This is the binary equivalent of 1562 in the ten-based system.

In the binary system, we have a very simple table of additions and multiplications:

$$0 + 0 = 0 \qquad 0 + 1 = 1 \qquad 1 + 1 = 10$$
$$0 \times 0 = 0 \qquad 0 \times 1 = 0 \qquad 1 \times 1 = 1$$

That is the entire list.

Thus, in the binary system:

$$
\begin{array}{r}
11 \\
+ \ 11 \\
\hline
10 \\
10 \\
\hline
110
\end{array}
\qquad
\begin{array}{r}
11 \\
\times \ 11 \\
\hline
11 \\
11 \\
\hline
1001
\end{array}
$$

You can check this, if you wish, by noticing that the binary 11, 110, and 1001 are equal to 3, 6, and 9 respectively in the ten-based system.

Now suppose you had a computing machine with a row of electronic switches (such as tubes or transistors). Each switch can have one of two positions. It can be ON (with current passing through) or OFF (with current not passing through).

Suppose now that the ON position is allowed to represent 1 and the OFF position 0. In that case, the computer can be so designed that the electrical manipulation of ONs and OFFs in the various switches follow the rules that govern the additions, multiplications, and other manipulations of the 1's and 0's in the binary system.

Such computers will shift patterns (according to binary rules) so rapidly that computations which would take human mathematicians months to perform can be worked out in a matter of minutes.

However, we have gotten off the direct line in this discussion of the various number systems. Let us return to the ten-based system and stay there henceforward.

JUGGLING EXPONENTS

To see how these ten-based exponential numbers can be manipulated it will be easier (and clearer) to use somewhat smaller numbers than the large one with which I started this chapter.

For instance, suppose we were dealing with the number 3200 and wished to express it in ten-based exponentials. We could use integers only and then 3200 would become $(3 \times 1000) + (2 \times 100)$, or $(3 \times 10^3) + (2 \times 10^2)$. However, it is far more convenient to use a single exponential whenever possible and this can be done by making use of decimals. Thus, you can express 3200 as 3.2×1000 (perform the multiplication and check this for yourself, if you wish), or 3.2×10^3.

It is possible, of course, to represent 3200 also as 32×100, which could be expressed exponentially as

32×10^2. Or it could be written as 0.32×10000 and then it would be 0.32×10^4. All three exponentials, 32×10^2, 3.2×10^3, and 0.32×10^4, are, indeed, identical. This can be shown by performing the multiplications indicated and getting 3200 in each case. It can also be shown without performing multiplications.

Consider, for instance, that $40 \times 50 = 2000$. Suppose now that you divided one of the numbers involved in the multiplication by 2 and multiplied the other by 2. This would give you either 20×100, or 80×25. In either case, the answer is still 2000. Suppose you multiplied one of the numbers by 10 and divided the other by 10. The problem would become either 4×500, or 400×5. In either case, the answer would still be 2000.

In other words, when two numbers are multiplied, the over-all value is not changed if one of the numbers is multiplied and the other divided by the same number. What is taken from one is given to the other.

Now consider again the number 3.2×10^3. Suppose we multiply 3.2 by 10 and divide 10^3 by 10; that, as I have just said, will not change the over-all value of the number. Multiplying 3.2 by 10 gives 32, of course. Dividing 10^3 by 10 (really 10^1, exponentially speaking) gives us 10^2, since in dividing we subtract exponents. The number, therefore, becomes 32×10^2 without any change in value.

We could work it the other way and divide 3.2 by 10 (giving 0.32) while multiplying 10^3 by 10 (giving 10^4). The number would become 0.32×10^4, still without change in value.

But since 32×10^2, 3.2×10^3, and 0.32×10^4 are all the same number, is there any reason why we should choose one form over the other? Mathematically, no. For the sake of convenience, however, it is customary to choose that form of the number in which the nonexponential portion lies between 1 and 10. In 32×10^2, the nonexponential part (32) is over 10, while in 0.32×10^4, the nonexponential part (0.32) is under 1. Therefore, 3.2×10^3, with 3.2 lying between 1 and 10, is the form of the number ordinarily used.

Except for the detail of the negative exponent, all this works the same for numbers less than 1. Take, for example, 0.0054. This can be expressed as 54×0.0001, or 5.4×0.001, or 0.54×0.01. Each of these multiplications, if carried out, will give 0.0054. Exponentially, these can be written 54×10^{-4}, 5.4×10^{-3} or 0.54×10^{-2}.

Again these numbers are equivalent. Beginning with 5.4×10^{-3}, you can multiply 5.4 by 10 and divide 10^{-3} by 10. Of course, $5.4 \times 10 = 54$; and $10^{-3} \div 10^1$ is 10^{-4}, since, once again, division involves subtraction of exponents and $-3 - 1$ is -4. So the number is changed to 54×10^{-4} without any change in value.

In the same way, dividing 5.4 by 10 and multiplying 10^{-3} by 10 will give 0.54×10^{-2} without change in value. And again, the preferred form is 5.4×10^{-3} because that is the one in which the nonexponential part of the number lies between 1 and 10.

JUGGLING EXPONENTIALS FURTHER

All the operations to which ordinary numbers may be subjected can be applied to exponential numbers as well.

In addition and subtraction, only the non-exponential parts of the number are involved. For instance, the sum of 2.3×10^4 and 4.2×10^4 is 6.5×10^4. (You can check this by converting the exponentials being added into ordinary numbers — 23,000 and 42,000 — adding them to get 65,000 and changing that back to an exponential. You can do the same for all the examples I give you. It will give you good practice in not necessarily believing what you are told, even when it is in print.)

The sum of 8.7×10^4 and 3.9×10^4 comes out to be 12.6×10^4. This answer can be left in that form. However, the nonexponential part is greater than 10. By the appropriate division-multiplication discussed in the previous section, you can convert the number to 1.26×10^5 which is just as correct an answer and is in the preferable form.

What, however, if the exponential portions of two numbers being added are not the same? What is the sum of 1.87×10^4 and 9×10^2? In order to get the sum, the exponential portions of the numbers must be made equal. For instance, 1.87×10^4 can be converted by the usual method to 187×10^2. When that is done the sum becomes $(187 \times 10^2) + (9 \times 10^2)$ and the answer is obviously 196×10^2.

The other possibility is that 9×10^2 can be converted to 0.09×10^4 (by now you don't need the details, I hope) and the sum becomes $(1.87 \times 10^4) + (0.09 \times 10^4) = 1.96 \times 10^4$.

So you have two possible answers: 196×10^2 and 1.96×10^4. But these are identical in value and it is the second form that is preferable.

Subtraction works just as addition does, but in reverse.

Actually, however, exponentials are rarely used for purposes of addition or subtraction. It is no easier to handle exponentials in addition or subtraction than it is to handle ordinary numbers. Less easy, in fact, because you must keep converting exponentials from one power to another.

Multiplication and division are another matter.

Suppose you wanted to multiply 60000 by 0.008. It looks easy enough and can be done as follows:

$$\begin{array}{r} 60000 \\ \times\ 0.008 \\ \hline 480.000 \end{array}$$

The only difficulty is that you have to keep track of the zeros and make sure you have the decimal point in the right place. (It is easy to slip up in these respects.)

Now let's convert both numbers into exponentials. First, 60000 is 6×10^4, while 0.008 is 8×10^{-3}. Multiplied, these are $6 \times 10^4 \times 8 \times 10^{-3}$. Since it doesn't matter in which order numbers are multiplied, this can be written as $6 \times 8 \times 10^4 \times 10^{-3}$. Well, 6×8 is obviously 48 while $10^4 \times 10^{-3}$ is 10^1. (You add exponents and $4 + (-3) = 1$.) The answer is 48×10^1 or, if written in the preferable form, 4.8×10^2. In either case, the exponential has the value of 480 in ordinary numbers, which is, of course, the right answer.

But the exponential operation has taken care of the zeros and the position of the decimal point for you. Furthermore, the task of keeping track of zeros and decimal points becomes more tedious as numbers grow larger or smaller, while exponentials can handle numbers of any size with equal ease.

Suppose, for instance, I were to ask you this: If the earth were made up exclusively of hydrogen atoms, how many hydrogen atoms would it contain?

The mass of the earth is 6000000000000000000000-0000000 grams and the mass of the hydrogen atom is 0.000000000000000000000000166 grams. To get the answer you must divide the mass of the earth by the mass of the hydrogen atom; i.e., 6000000000000000-000000000000 ÷ 0.000000000000000000000000166. You may do this if you wish.

However if you use exponentials, the problem becomes $(6 \times 10^{27}) \div (1.66 \times 10^{-24})$. As in multiplication, you can change this to a division of one nonexponential part by the other and one exponential part by the other. The quotient of $6 \div 1.66$ is 3.6 (not exactly but close enough); while $10^{27} \div 10^{-24} = 10^{51}$. The number of hydrogen atoms in the earth (if the earth were entirely hydrogen) would therefore be 3.6×10^{51}. This would be 3600000000-000000000000000000000000000000000000000000 in ordinary numbers and is what you would have obtained if you had performed the division given in the previous paragraph.

Powers and roots of exponential numbers are of no particular difficulty. Thus, $(9 \times 10^4)^2$ is equal to $9^2 \times (10^4)^2$ which comes out to 81×10^8 or, preferably, 8.1×10^9. On the other hand $\sqrt{9 \times 10^4}$ is equal to $\sqrt{9} \times \sqrt{10^4}$ or 3×10^2.

EXPONENTS TAKE OVER COMPLETELY

There is still room for impatience in the use of exponentials in multiplication and division. It is all right for numbers with many zeros, but suppose we want to multiply 6837 by 1822. If we convert them into exponentials, they become 6.837×10^3 and 1.822×10^3. Multiplying the exponential portions is easy but what about multiplying the nonexponential portions, 6.837 and 1.822? This is just our original problem all over again, with nothing more than the added complication of a decimal point to keep track of.

What we want, in other words, is a ten-based number in which the easily handled exponential part does as much of the work as possible and the troublesome nonexponential part as little as possible. Best of all would be a ten-based number that was all exponential with the nonexponential part completely eliminated. That brings us to the matter of decimal exponents I discussed at the end of Chapter 7.

Let's take a closer look at ten-based exponentials. To begin with, $10^0 = 1$ and $10^1 = 10$. What about exponents *between* 0 and 1? For instance, $10^{0.5}$ is $10^{\frac{1}{2}}$ or $\sqrt{10}$ which is, approximately, 3.162278. In similar fashion (but more complicatedly) the values of 10 to other decimal powers can be obtained. Elaborate tables of such values exist in various reference books. I will give a short one here of the values of decimal powers of 10.

Usually, since the base 10 is taken for granted, only the exponent is listed in the tables. The exponent standing alone is called the "logarithm." The value of the exponential in ordinary figures is the "antilogarithm." As an example, in the expression $10^2 = 100$, 2 is the logarithm of 100, and 100 is the antilogarithm of 2. A table, such as the one that follows, that gives the antilogarithms for a regular series of logarithms is an "antilogarithm table."

A small antilogarithm table

exponential	logarithm	antilogarithm
$10^{0.0}$	0.0	1.000
$10^{0.1}$	0.1	1.259
$10^{0.2}$	0.2	1.585
$10^{0.3}$	0.3	1.995
$10^{0.4}$	0.4	2.512
$10^{0.5}$	0.5	3.162
$10^{0.6}$	0.6	3.981
$10^{0.7}$	0.7	5.012
$10^{0.8}$	0.8	6.310
$10^{0.9}$	0.9	7.943
$10^{1.0}$	1.0	10.000

The antilogarithms in the table are, of course, not exact, and can't be exact, since, except for even values of powers of ten, like $10^{0.0}$ and $10^{1.0}$, all the powers are irrational (that is, they cannot be expressed as exact fractions). However, the antilogarithms can be carried out to as many decimal places as may be useful.

If we take this in reverse, we can express any number between 1 and 10 as some decimal power of ten. In other words, for every number it is possible to work out its equivalent logarithm by means of computations we needn't go into in this book.

Here is a small table, for instance, of logarithms for a regular series of ordinary numbers. Much more elaborate tables, giving the values of many more numbers, can be found in various reference books.

The result is that no one calculates logarithms any longer. The job has been done. Now it is only necessary to look them up in tables. Using the small logarithm table given here, for instance, you can see that the logarithm of 3.2 (to take a number at random) is 0.5051, while the logarithm of 2.4 (to take another) is 0.3802. (These values are, of course, only approximate, as are all logarithms except those of integral powers of ten.)

A small logarithm table

number	logarithm	number	logarithm
1.0	0.0000	1.3	0.1139
1.1	0.0414	1.4	0.1461
1.2	0.0792	1.5	0.1761

number	logarithm	number	logarithm
1.6	0.2041	4.3	0.6335
1.7	0.2304	4.4	0.6435
1.8	0.2553	4.5	0.6532
1.9	0.2788	4.6	0.6628
2.0	0.3010	4.7	0.6721
2.1	0.3222	4.8	0.6812
2.2	0.3424	4.9	0.6902
2.3	0.3617	5.0	0.6990
2.4	0.3802	5.1	0.7076
2.5	0.3979	5.2	0.7160
2.6	0.4150	5.3	0.7243
2.7	0.4314	5.4	0.7324
2.8	0.4472	5.5	0.7404
2.9	0.4624	5.6	0.7482
3.0	0.4771	5.7	0.7559
3.1	0.4914	5.8	0.7634
3.2	0.5051	5.9	0.7709
3.3	0.5185	6.0	0.7782
3.4	0.5315	6.1	0.7853
3.5	0.5441	6.2	0.7924
3.6	0.5563	6.3	0.7993
3.7	0.5682	6.4	0.8062
3.8	0.5798	6.5	0.8129
3.9	0.5911	6.6	0.8195
4.0	0.6021	6.7	0.8261
4.1	0.6128	6.8	0.8325
4.2	0.6232	6.9	0.8388

number	logarithm	number	logarithm
7.0	0.8451	8.6	0.9345
7.1	0.8513	8.7	0.9395
7.2	0.8573	8.8	0.9445
7.3	0.8633	8.9	0.9494
7.4	0.8692	9.0	0.9542
7.5	0.8751	9.1	0.9590
7.6	0.8808	9.2	0.9638
7.7	0.8865	9.3	0.9685
7.8	0.8921	9.4	0.9731
7.9	0.8976	9.5	0.9777
8.0	0.9031	9.6	0.9823
8.1	0.9085	9.7	0.9868
8.2	0.9138	9.8	0.9912
8.3	0.9191	9.9	0.9956
8.4	0.9243	10.0	1.0000
8.5	0.9294		

Now here's the value of logarithms. They are really exponents, and in multiplying numbers, we need only add exponents. To multiply 3.2 and 2.4, we need only add 0.5051 and 0.3802 to get 0.8853. This is still an exponent, of course, and tells us only that we must find the value of $10^{0.8853}$ to get the answer. For such a value we search a sufficiently elaborate antilogarithm table and find the antilogarithm of 0.8853 to be 7.68, and that is the answer of 3.2 × 2.4.

On the other hand, to divide 3.2 by 2.4, we need
only subtract 0.3802 from 0.5051 and get 0.1249.
The antilogarithm of that is 1.333, which is the
answer.

Now suppose we return to the problem with which
we started the section: 6837 × 1822. Converting
these numbers to exponentials, we have 6.837×10^3
and 1.822×10^3. The logarithm of 10^3 is simply 3,
since a logarithm is merely the exponent of 10 that
gives the value of a certain number. Well, the
exponent of 10 that gives the value of 10^3 is obviously 3. In the same way, the logarithm of 10^{12} is
12 and the logarithm of 10^{-14} is -14.

The logarithm of 6.837 must be looked up in a
more elaborate table than the one given in this book
and turns out to be 0.83487. The logarithm of
6.837×10^3 is therefore 0.83487 + 3 (remember
when we multiply numbers, we *add* logarithms) or
3.83487.

In the same way, the logarithm of 1.822 turns out
to be 0.26055, so that the logarithm of 1.822×10^3
is 0.26055 + 3, or 3.26055.

Multiplying 6837 and 1822 is done, then, by
adding the logarithms 3.83487 + 3.26055, which
comes out to 7.09542. Let us change that to
0.09542 + 7 and find the antilogarithm. (The
decimal portion of a logarithm (0.09542, in this case)
is called the "mantissa," the integer portion (7, in

this case) the "characteristic.")

The antilogarithm of a whole number is simply the power of 10 to that number. Thus, the antilogarithm of 7 is 10^7. The antilogarithm of 0.09542 is 1.246 (as found in a table). The antilogarithm of 7.09542 is therefore 1.246×10^7 (in going from logarithm to antilogarithm, addition must be reconverted to multiplication, of course) or, in ordinary numbers, 12,460,000.

If you actually multiply 6837 by 1822, you'll find the answer comes out 12,457,014. However, remember that logarithms are not exact so that your answer can only be approximate.

Dividing 6837 by 1822 means that you must subtract logarithms. Since $3.83487 - 3.26055 = 0.57432$, for which the antilogarithm is 3.752, that is your answer. Actual division will place the answer closer to 3.75192 but again logarithms are only approximate.

Now you may be impatient with a method which yields only approximate results and which involves looking things up in two different tables, all in place of the familiar process of multiplication and division. But you see, practical problems in science or engineering often involve repeated multiplications and divisions. You may have to solve a problem such as $(194.768 \times 0.045 \times 19.2^2) \div (1.558 \times 35.4)$. Using ordinary multiplication and division, this would take a long time, whereas the person who is skilled in logarithms looks up a few figures in a table (and with practice this can be done quickly), adds, subtracts, looks up another figure and has the answer.

Moreover, if you are satisfied with answers that are almost exact, but not right on the nose — and often such "nearly right" answers can be very useful — there is an additional short cut.

THE NEW ABACUS

The clue to the short cut can be found in a close look at the way in which logarithms increase. Notice that the logarithm of 1.0 is 0.0000, that of 2.0 is 0.3010, and that of 3.0 is 0.4771. In going from 1 to 2, the value of the logarithm is increased by 0.3010; in going from 2 to 3, it is further increased by only 0.1761.

To continue, the logarithm of 4.0 is 0.6020, which means a further increase of only 0.1249. And in going from 9.0 to 10.0, the logarithm changes from 0.9542 to 1.0000, an increase of 0.0458, while in going from 19.0 to 20.0, the logarithm changes from 1.2788 to 1.3010, an increase of only 0.0222.

If one were to draw a scale on a straight edge showing logarithmic values evenly spaced and then, on the opposite edge, show the ordinary numbers (antilogarithms) placed in position corresponding

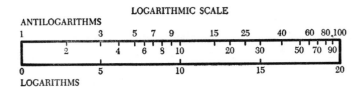

to the logarithms, the ordinary numbers would appear to squeeze together at the high end. You can see this in the accompanying figure. This is a reflection of the fact that with increasing numbers the rate of increase in the logarithms slows up.

Such a squeezed number scale corresponding to an even series of logarithms is called a "logarithmic scale." Mathematically, the logarithmic scale is used to construct a useful instrument. Two logarithmic scales may be brought together in such a way that one can be moved with respect to the other, as shown in the figure.

By moving the two scales, we can add numbers which, since they are arranged in a logarithmic scale, really amounts to adding the logarithms of the numbers indicated. This, in turn, means that we are multiplying the numbers themselves.

For instance, to multiply 2 and 3, move the 1 of the movable scale over the 2 of the stationary

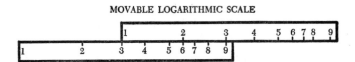

scale. If you move your eye to the 3 of the movable
scale, you have automatically added the logarithm
of 2 to that of 3 and, sure enough, under the 3 of the
movable scale is a 6 on the stationary scale. And,
you see, 2 × 3 = 6.

Such pieces of wood, ruled off with lines (hence a
"rule"), one of which can be slid with reference to
to the other, is a "slide rule."

An elaborate slide rule, such as that shown in the
sketch, has a number of different scales, finely and
accurately divided, which can be used to solve a
variety of problems as easily as that of 2 × 3.

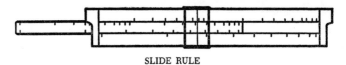

SLIDE RULE

Because a slide rule is actually a logarithm table
frozen on wood, it can solve any problem that
logarithms can solve with an accuracy depending
on how closely the divisions can be read.

Every gain has its compensating loss. A slide
rule makes logarithm tables unnecessary, yes, but
one of the virtues of the logarithm as ordinarily
handled is that it automatically takes care of the
decimal point. The slide rule does not.

To locate the decimal point in slide-rule work, it
is necessary first to make a quick estimate of the
answer to your problem. For instance, consider the

problem I presented a few pages ago:

$$(194.768 \times 0.045 \times 19.2^2) \div (1.558 \times 35.4)$$

By changing the figures to near-by "round figures," this can be transformed to: $\left(200 \times \dfrac{1}{20} \times 20^2\right) \div \left(1\dfrac{1}{2} \times 35\right)$, which works out to $4000 \div 50$, or 80. The answer, we thus know, should be somewhere closer to 80 than to 8 or 800, and that fixes the decimal point (or, as we sometimes say, it fixes the "order of magnitude").

Now, using my own slide rule, I can manipulate the movable scale back and forth, adding and subtracting logarithms, and find the numerals of the answer come out 587. Since I know the answer must be closer to 80 than to 8 or 800, I place the decimal point so as to make the number read 58.7. The whole process took me 35 seconds, and at that, I worked slowly to make sure I made no mistake.

To solve the problem by ordinary arithmetical manipulation would give me a more accurate answer. I have worked it out to get 58.6, but in the process I made two mistakes which had to be corrected. In all, it took me 20 minutes and at that I cheated. In the first place, I found out I had made a mistake by the fact that my arithmetical answer did not agree with my slide-rule answer. And then, I located my mistakes and avoided having to

repeat the entire problem by checking each indi-
vidual step against the slide rule.

Modern computers, of course, work far more
accurately and quickly than slide rules, but they
are not portable. It will be a long time before the
engineer or scientist will feel comfortable without
a slide rule within easy reach. Sometimes, I think
the modern scientist is the reincarnation of the
ancient scribe, and his slide rule the reincarnation
of the ancient abacus.

9
9
9

From Number Line to Number Area
9

So FAR, in all my discussion of square roots, I have carefully avoided mentioning negative numbers. For instance, I say that $\sqrt{4}$ is 2 because $2 \times 2 = 4$. But, by the same token, $\sqrt{4}$ must also be -2, since $-2 \times -2 = 4$. (Remember that negative times negative gives positive.)

Actually, then, there are two possible square roots of 4 and, properly speaking, this is what should be written: $\sqrt{4} = \pm 2$. The symbol $\pm$ is read "plus or minus."

But now if $+2$ and -2 are both the square root of $+4$, what is the square root of -4? What number multiplied by itself is equal to -4? To be sure, $+2 \times -2 = -4$, but $+2$ and -2 are not the same number so, in multiplying them, neither is being "multiplied by itself."

It would seem as though there is no number anywhere, either positive or negative, that can possibly be the square root of −4 or of any negative number. However, just to be stubborn, let's consider the problem for a while.

First, let's make the problem as simple as we can. A number like $\sqrt{64}$ can be broken up into factors so that it can be written as $\sqrt{16 \times 4}$. In turn this can be transformed into $\sqrt{16} \times \sqrt{4}$. Separating it into two square roots doesn't affect the value since $\sqrt{64}$ is 8 and $\sqrt{16} \times \sqrt{4}$ is 4×2, which is 8.

Repeated trials will show that if a number is broken up into factors, then the square root of the original number is equal to the product of the square roots of the factors. This is true of irrationals, too. For instance, consider $\sqrt{15}$ and $\sqrt{5} \times \sqrt{3}$. You can look up the appropriate square roots in tables and find that $\sqrt{15}$ is 3.872983, $\sqrt{5}$ is 2.236068 and $\sqrt{3}$ is 1.732051 (approximately, of course). Since 2.236068×1.732051 does indeed turn out to be equal to just about 3.872983, then $\sqrt{15} = \sqrt{5} \times \sqrt{3}$.

Very well, then: Any negative number can be considered as being the product of the corresponding positive number and −1. In other words, $-64 = 64 \times -1$; $-276 = 276 \times -1$; $-1.98 = 1.98 \times -1$, and so on.

The square root of any negative number, say −172, can therefore be broken up as follows: $\sqrt{-172} = \sqrt{172 \times -1} = \sqrt{172} \times \sqrt{-1}$.

In short, if we only knew the square root of
minus one ($\sqrt{-1}$) we could work out the square
root of any negative number. But here we are
faced with the dilemma already mentioned: $1 \times
1 = 1$ and $-1 \times -1 = 1$. No number multiplied
by itself will give -1.

The only thing we can do is *invent* an answer.
We could, for instance, define a sign such as $\#$ and say
that $\# \times \#$ gives a negative number. Then $\#1 \times
\#1 = -1$. That would be true by definition and if
it didn't contradict anything else already established
in the mathematical scheme, there would be no
reason why we couldn't get away with this.

Of course, such a number would seem to be an
imaginary one. We know what $+\$1$ and $-\$1$ are.
The first is a one-dollar asset and the latter a one-
dollar debt. What would $\#\$1$ be? The first mathe-
maticians who worked with the square roots of
negative numbers called them "imaginary numbers"
and the name persists to this day. Ordinary
numbers, whether positive or negative, rational or
irrational, are called "real numbers" in contra-
distinction.

The mathematicians have not made up a new
sign, however, corresponding to $+$ or $-$. (I wish
they had; it would have been neater.) Instead,
they invented the symbol **i** (for "imaginary") and
let that stand for the square root of -1. In other

words, $\sqrt{-1} = \mathbf{i}$, and, of course, this means that $\mathbf{i} \times \mathbf{i} = \mathbf{i}^2 = -1$. To be sure, $-\mathbf{i} \times -\mathbf{i}$ is also equal to $\mathbf{i}^2$ or -1, so we must really write $\sqrt{-1} = -\mathbf{i}$. And, to round off the matter, $\mathbf{i} \times -\mathbf{i} = -\mathbf{i}^2 = -(-1) = 1$.

And now we have the answer for all square roots of negative numbers. The value of $\sqrt{-4}$ is equal to $\sqrt{4} \times \sqrt{-1}$, or to $2 \times \mathbf{i}$, which can be written simply $2\mathbf{i}$ or, more properly, $\pm 2\mathbf{i}$. In the same way, the value of $\sqrt{-64}$ is $\pm 8\mathbf{i}$, while the value of $\sqrt{-15}$ is $\pm\sqrt{15}\mathbf{i}$ or, approximately $\pm 3.872983\mathbf{i}$.

NUMBERS AND COMPASS POINTS

However, you may, by now, be bursting with indignation. Never mind all this talk about $\mathbf{i}$, you may be thinking. What does $\mathbf{i}$ *mean?*

Actually, it can mean whatever we choose to make it mean. You must remember that numbers are only a creation of man to help him understand the universe about him. We can do what we want with our own creations as long as it helps us understand.

For instance, the ancient Greeks couldn't see what -1 meant; it was just as mysterious to them as $\sqrt{-1}$ would have been. I tried to explain -1 by means of a vertical line marked off with positive numbers above the zero and negative numbers below the zero (see Chapter 2).

That seemed to work, so let's go back to that. Suppose we draw another line through the zero point of that first line, this new line being horizontal. Let us mark off the horizontal line at intervals equal to those used already on the vertical line. To the right, we mark the intervals $+i$, $+2i$, $+3i$, $+4i$, and so on. To the left, we mark them off as $-i$, $-2i$, $-3i$, $-4i$, and so on. The accompanying figure shows this.

Now we can see what the term i means. We agreed to let $+1$ mean a mile north of a town (for instance) and -1 a mile south of a town. Well,

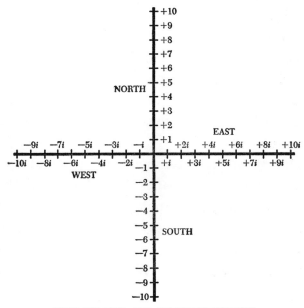

LINES FOR REAL AND IMAGINARY NUMBERS

then, $+i$ is a mile east of a town and $-i$ is a mile west of a town. (This is not what the numbers "really" mean. There is no "real" meaning. It is only a picture designed to help us grasp the abstract relationship in terms of something concrete.)

For instance, instead of using symbols such as $+$ and $-$, we could have decided to name numbers after the initials of the points of the compass. We could have decided to call positive real numbers "N numbers" (for "north"), negative real numbers "S numbers" (for "south"), positive imaginary numbers "E numbers" (for "east") and negative imaginary numbers "W numbers" (for "west").

On this basis, there would be no reason to call N and S numbers "real" while E and W numbers were "imaginary." The four points of the compass are all equally real. However, the name "imaginary" arose for historical reasons and it is too late to change it now.

Using these "compass numbers" to build up a self-consistent mathematics (which is all that mathematicians really are trying to do) it might prove to be necessary to say that:

N×N = N	S×N = S	E×N = E	W×N = W
N×S = S	S×S = N	E×S = W	W×S = E
N×E = E	S×E = W	E×E = S	W×E = N
N×W = W	S×W = E	E×W = N	W×W = S

This arrangement (a kind of multiplication table for signs) is the one we actually work with in the mathematics that has been invented by mankind. This multiplication table may look odd, but it has a simple geometrical significance, as you'll see if you study the figure.

This does not mean that ours is the only "true"

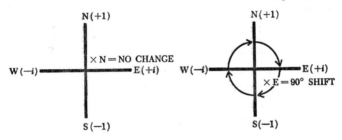

MULTIPLYING BY N ROTATES THE DIRECTION 0°;

$E \times N = E$
$S \times N = S$
$W \times N = W$
$N \times N = N$

MULTIPLYING BY E ROTATES THE DIRECTION 90° CLOCKWISE;

$E \times E = S$
$S \times E = W$
$W \times E = N$
$N \times E = E$

mathematics or that some other arrangement might not be equally "true." It just happens to be the arrangement that has proven useful to us and is the one that is used.

MORE COMPASS POINTS

As long as we're talking of north, south, east, and west, what about a direction like northeast or southeast? So far in our multiplications of real and imaginary numbers, the answer has always come out on one of the two lines, north–south or east–west.

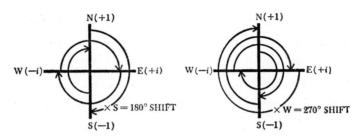

MULTIPLYING BY S ROTATES THE   MULTIPLYING BY W ROTATES THE
DIRECTION 180°;   DIRECTION 270°;

$$E \times S = W$$ $$E \times W = N$$
$$S \times S = N$$ $$S \times W = E$$
$$W \times S = E$$ $$W \times W = S$$
$$N \times S = S$$ $$N \times W = W$$

N = POSITIVE REAL NUMBERS, SUCH AS +1

E = POSITIVE IMAGINARIES, SUCH AS +i

S = NEGATIVE REAL NUMBERS, SUCH AS —1

W = NEGATIVE IMAGINARIES, SUCH AS —i

What about addition, though? What is the sum
of 1 and i?

Mathematicians haven't found it necessary to
invent symbols that will represent such a sum and
they leave it simply as 1 + i. However, this sum
can be made to have meaning on our directional
number system. Let's draw the north–south and
east–west lines again and, instead of just making
numbered marks on the lines, let's draw new lines
through each mark.

Suppose that through every mark on the vertical
line of real numbers, we draw a light horizontal line.
The horizontal line that goes through +1 is +1 all
along its length at every point. The horizontal line

that goes through $+2$ is $+2$ all along its length, while the one going through -3 is -3 all along the line and so on.

Let's do the same for the horizontal line of imaginary numbers, drawing light vertical lines through every marking. Again, the vertical line through $+2i$ will be $+2i$ all along its length, the one through $-5i$ will be $-5i$ all along its length, and so on.

When this is done, as shown in the figure, we have a checkerboard pattern with the line of each imaginary number crossing the line of each real number and vice versa.

Now we can get the answer to the question con-

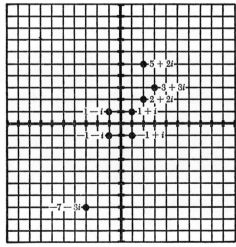

COMPLEX NUMBERS

cerning the sum of $1 + i$. A number such as $1 + i$ would represent a point that is both $+1$ and $+i$ and that point can only be where the $+1$ and $+i$ lines cross in the checkerboard pattern. Since the intervals are equal on both lines, $1 + i$ represents a number in the northeast direction. So do $2 + 2i$, $3 + 3i$, $4 + 4i$, and so on.

A number like $1 - i$ can be written as $+1 + (-i)$ and the point representing it would be where the $+1$ and $-i$ lines cross, and would lie in a northwest direction. Similarly $-1 + i$ would be in the southeast and $-1 - i$ in the southwest.

Other directions could be represented by such numbers as $5 + 2i$, $-7 - 3i$, and so on. In fact, every position on the checkerboard pattern (which can be imagined as extending out in every direction indefinitely) can be regarded as a point representing some number which is the sum of a real and an imaginary number. What's more, the position could have decimal or even irrational values and lie between the checkerboard lines as $9.54 + 0.015i$ or $2\sqrt{7} - 5\sqrt{2}\,i$.

Numbers of this type, including a real part and an imaginary part, are called "complex numbers." As a matter of fact, numbers that are entirely real or entirely imaginary might also be considered as complex numbers. The number 42, for instance, could be written as $42 + 0i$, while the number $-5i$

could be written as $0 - 5i$.

The importance of complex numbers in practical affairs is that they state not only magnitude as ordinary numbers do, but also direction.

To give one example, in physics and engineering, "forces" play an important role. Forces are pushes and pulls. There are strong forces, weak ones, and those in between. The amount of force can be measured in real numbers alone, with pushes positive, for instance, and pulls negative.

But forces also have direction. A push or pull can be up, down, sideways, or anything in between. And for both number and direction, complex numbers are needed. In this way, the number i, which to many nonmathematicians seems completely mysterious and useless, is really down to earth. In electronics, for instance, there would be no possibility of mathematical treatment without i. Alternating currents constantly change, both in amount and direction, and to express these changes in both respects mathematically, complex numbers must be used.

Complex numbers can be added and subtracted as ordinary numbers can be, the real parts and the imaginary parts being added or subtracted separately. Thus if $+2 - 4i$ is added to $-5 + 7i$, the answer is $-3 + 3i$, while if it is subtracted, the answer is $-7 + 11i$. (This can be demonstrated on the checkerboard pattern as ordinary addition and subtraction can be shown on the north–south line, but perhaps you can do that for yourself now.)

Multiplication is more complicated but no more complicated really than the multiplication of ordinary numbers. When multiplying 35 by 28, as I explained in Chapter 3, 35 is broken up into 30 + 5, and 28 into 20 + 8. Each part of one number was then multiplied by each part of the other and the submultiples were added up.

Exactly this is done in dealing with complex numbers. To multiply 3 + 5i by 6 + i, you set up the following pattern:

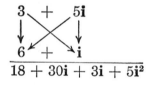

$$18 + 30i + 3i + 5i^2$$

By following the arrows and multiplying each above by each below we see that: 3×6 is 18; $3 \times i$ is 3i; $5i \times 6$ is 30i; and $5i \times i$ is $5i^2$. Since $i^2 = -1$, $5i^2 = -5$.

Two of the submultiples are real. These, 18 and -5, if added together, make 13. The other two, 30i and 3i are imaginary and if added together make 33i. The answer to our multiplication of complex numbers is 13 + 33i.

Other types of arithmetical manipulation can also

be demonstrated in similar fashion. Complex numbers, to put it briefly, can be handled by the same tools that will handle ordinary numbers, and are therefore no more mysterious.

DIGGING MORE DEEPLY FOR ROOTS

The field of complex numbers makes it possible to consider some facts about the higher roots.

I have already explained that the square root of any number has two solutions so that $\sqrt{+1}$ is either $+1$ or -1 and $\sqrt{-1}$ is either $+i$ or $-i$.

What about $\sqrt[4]{+1}$? Obviously, $+1 \times +1 \times +1 \times +1 = +1$, so $+1$ is one of the fourth roots of $+1$. Then, suppose we consider $-1 \times -1 \times -1 \times -1$. The first two terms multiplied together yield $+1$, and so do the last two, so $-1 \times -1 \times -1 \times -1$ is the same as $+1 \times +1$, which is $+1$. Therefore, -1 is a second fourth root of $+1$.

But we are not done. What about $+i \times +i \times +i \times +i$? The product of $+i$ and $+i$ is -1, so the quadruple multiplication is equivalent to -1×-1, which is $+1$. Consequently $+i$ is a fourth root of $+1$. By the same reasoning, you can show that $-i$ is a fourth root of $+1$.

The conclusion is that $\sqrt[4]{+1}$ has four answers: $+1$, -1, $+i$, and $-i$. Similarly, you can show that $\sqrt[4]{-1}$ has four answers: $+\sqrt{+i}$, $-\sqrt{+i}$, $+\sqrt{-i}$, and $-\sqrt{-i}$. You might ask what $\sqrt{+i}$ is. To this the answer is: It is a number which, when multiplied by itself, gives **i**. For that reason $+\sqrt{+\mathbf{i}} \times +\sqrt{+\mathbf{i}}$ is equal to $+\mathbf{i}$, and $+\sqrt{+\mathbf{i}} \times +\sqrt{+\mathbf{i}} \times +\sqrt{+\mathbf{i}} \times +\sqrt{+\mathbf{i}}$ can be transformed into $+\mathbf{i} \times +\mathbf{i}$, which is, in turn, equal to -1. Hence $+\sqrt{+\mathbf{i}}$ is one of the fourth roots of -1, and by similar reasoning, so are $-\sqrt{+\mathbf{i}}$, $+\sqrt{-\mathbf{i}}$, and $-\sqrt{-\mathbf{i}}$.

In the same way, every number can be shown to have four fourth roots.

But if every number has two square roots and four fourth roots, will it also have three cube roots, five fifth roots, forty-two forty-second roots and so on? Actually, this is so, though it takes more advanced mathematics to prove it than can be dealt with in this book.

However, we can check the theory on cube roots, anyway. What, for instance, is $\sqrt[3]{+1}$? Well, to begin with, $+1 \times +1 \times +1 = +1$, so that $+1$ is one of the cube roots of $+1$.

But where are the other two? If we go into negatives, we might try $-1 \times -1 \times -1$. However, $-1 \times -1 = +1$, so $-1 \times -1 \times -1$ can be transformed to $+1 \times -1$, and that is equal to -1. Therefore, -1 is *not* one of the cube roots of $+1$. Furthermore any real number other than $+1$ or -1, or any imaginary other than $+\mathbf{i}$ or $-\mathbf{i}$ would not give the quantity 1 (of any sign) if cubed.

Where, then, are the missing two cube roots of $+1$? Do they exist?

Yes, they do, but in the field of complex numbers. Without describing the method for finding them, I shall simply present the complex numbers $-\frac{1}{2} + \frac{1}{2}\sqrt{3}\,\mathbf{i}$ and $-\frac{1}{2} - \frac{1}{2}\sqrt{3}\,\mathbf{i}$ as the missing roots. We can check this, too.

If $-\frac{1}{2} + \frac{1}{2}\sqrt{3}\,\mathbf{i}$ is one of the cube roots of $+1$, then $\left(-\frac{1}{2} + \frac{1}{2}\sqrt{3}\,\mathbf{i}\right)^3$ or $\left(-\frac{1}{2} + \frac{1}{2}\sqrt{3}\,\mathbf{i}\right) \times \left(-\frac{1}{2} + \frac{1}{2}\sqrt{3}\,\mathbf{i}\right) \times \left(-\frac{1}{2} + \frac{1}{2}\sqrt{3}\,\mathbf{i}\right)$ should be equal to $+1$. We can perform the first multiplication as described a few pages above:

$$-\frac{1}{2} + \frac{1}{2}\sqrt{3}\,\mathbf{i}$$
$$-\frac{1}{2} + \frac{1}{2}\sqrt{3}\,\mathbf{i}$$
$$\overline{+\frac{1}{4} - \frac{1}{4}\sqrt{3}\,\mathbf{i} - \frac{1}{4}\sqrt{3}\,\mathbf{i} + \frac{3}{4}\mathbf{i}^2}$$

The two imaginary submultiples, $-\frac{1}{4}\sqrt{3}\,\mathbf{i}$ and

$-\dfrac{1}{4}\sqrt{3}\,\mathbf{i}$, add up, of course, to $-\dfrac{1}{2}\sqrt{3}\,\mathbf{i}$. As for

$+\dfrac{3}{4}\,\mathbf{i}^2$, that is really a real number, since $\mathbf{i}^2 = -1$,

so that $+\dfrac{3}{4}\,\mathbf{i}^2 = -3/4$. That and the other real

submultiple, $+\dfrac{1}{4}$, add up to $-\dfrac{1}{2}$. The product of

this multiplication turns out to be $-\dfrac{1}{2}-\dfrac{1}{2}\sqrt{3}\,\mathbf{i}$.

It is next necessary to multiply this product once

again by $-\dfrac{1}{2}+\dfrac{1}{2}\sqrt{3}\,\mathbf{i}$ as shown here.

$$-\frac{1}{2} \quad - \quad \frac{1}{2}\sqrt{3}\,\mathbf{i}$$
$$-\frac{1}{2} \quad + \quad \frac{1}{2}\sqrt{3}\,\mathbf{i}$$
$$\overline{+\frac{1}{4}+\frac{1}{4}\sqrt{3}\,\mathbf{i}-\frac{1}{4}\sqrt{3}\,\mathbf{i}-\frac{3}{4}\mathbf{i}^2}$$

The two imaginary submultiples, $+\dfrac{1}{4}\sqrt{3}\,\mathbf{i}$ and

$-\dfrac{1}{4}\sqrt{3}\,\mathbf{i}$, add up to 0 and can be forgotten. The

number $-\dfrac{3}{4}\,\mathbf{i}^2$ is actually real and, since $\mathbf{i}^2 = -1$,

turns out to be $+\dfrac{3}{4}$. Add this to the remaining

submultiple, $+\dfrac{1}{4}$, and the grand total of the cubing

turns out to be $+1$.

The same process can be carried through for $-\frac{1}{2} - \frac{1}{2}\sqrt{3}\ \mathbf{i}$, and both it and $-\frac{1}{2} + \frac{1}{2}\sqrt{3}\ \mathbf{i}$ are therefore cube roots of $+1$.

It can also be shown that -1 has three cube roots, as well as $\mathbf{i}$ and $-\mathbf{i}$. In each case two of the roots are complex numbers.

BEYOND i

It is also possible to imagine a third line (or "axis") in our checkerboard figure, so that we have not only north, south, east and west, but also in and out. This gives us a solid figure and, instead of forming a checkerboard of squares, we can form a mosaic of cubes.

The third axis consists of "hyperimaginaries" which are symbolized as j. The numbers along the third axis, in other words, are $+1j$, $+2j$, $+3j$, and so on in one direction and $-1j$, $-2j$, $-3j$, and so on in the other.

It is then possible to locate any number in space by means of the crossing point of a north–south plane, an east–west plane and an in–out plane. (Cubes are formed of the intersections of planes just as the squares of the checkerboard were formed of the intersections of lines.) A point in space might be represented as $+5 + 2\mathbf{i} - 4j$, and such a number is a "hypercomplex number."

Although no more than three axes can be visualized in the world as we know it, since there are only three dimensions to our ordinary way of thinking, mathematicians can imagine more dimensions. They can even work with systems of axes, where the exact number is not specified. They then speak of "n-dimensional space," the *n* standing for "any number."

10

10

10

Endlessness

10

THE "NOT-A-NUMBER"

ANYONE THINKING ABOUT NUMBERS must come to the conclusion that there are a great many of them, and feel at a loss to express just how many. In poetry, one could make use of some simile: "as many as the sands of the sea"; "as numerous as the stars that shine and twinkle in the Milky Way."

To the mathematician, however, similes are of no use. To him, it merely seems that the integers are formed by beginning with one, adding one to that for the next number, and one to that for the next number, and so on. Since the mathematical rules do not set any limits to addition (*any* two numbers may be added) there can be no end to this process. After all, however large a number is named — *however* large — though it stretch in a line of small figures from here to the farthest star, it is always possible to say "that number plus one" and have a still higher number.

The series of integers, if written in order, 1, 2, 3

... is "infinite," a word coming from Latin words meaning "no end." Consequently, when we can write the series of numbers thus: 1, 2, 3 ... , we mean "1, 2, 3, and so on endlessly."

In the same way if we consider the negative numbers, -1, -2, -3, and so on, we can see that they too go on forever and can be written: -1, -2, -3 ... Similarly, the series of positive imaginaries may be written as $+1i$, $+2i$, $+3i$ ... , and the negative imaginaries as $-1i$, $-2i$, $-3i$ ...

Now let's consider another kind of series of integers. Let's think of the even numbers: 2, 4, 6, 8, and so on. How many even numbers are there?

One way of arguing this question would be to say: Well, the integers can be divided into odd numbers and even numbers alternately, so that in the first ten numbers there are five odds and five evens, in the first hundred numbers there are fifty odds and fifty evens, and so on. This sort of thing would go on no matter how many integers are taken. Therefore, the total number of even integers is half the total number of all integers.

But this is not so. The number of integers is infinite, and one cannot talk of "a half of infinity."

Instead, consider the even integers this way. The series 2, 4, 6, 8 ... can continue endlessly. There is no "largest even number" any more than there is a "largest number." For though you name an even number written in small numerals from here to the farthest star, it is always possible to say "that number plus two." Hence the series of even numbers should be written: 2, 4, 6 . . .

In the same way, odd numbers are 1, 3, 5 . . . ; the series of numbers, counting by fives, are 5, 10, 15 . . . ; and the series of numbers counting by millions are 1000000, 2000000, 3000000 . . . All these series of integers are endless and that is all that infinity (or an infinite number) means.

COUNTING WITHOUT COUNTING

But this may not satisfy you. Surely, you may be thinking, even though the series of even numbers is endless and the series of all integers is endless, the fact still remains that there are only half as many even numbers as there are all integers, and that there are only a millionth as many even-million numbers. It stands to reason!

(Never trust an argument *only* because it stands to reason. It stands to reason that if a man is facing north, his back is toward the south. However, if he's standing at the South Pole and is facing north, his back is also toward the north.)

Well, then, let's settle the matter by finding out how many even numbers there are compared with

all the integers. How, if the quantity is endless?
Why, we'll count.

Let's first see what we mean by counting. In
the ordinary meaning of the word, we count objects
by assigning each one a number in succession. This
object is number one, that is number two, the other
is number three, and so on. When we finish, if the
last object was assigned number ten, then there are
ten objects.

But can we count without numbers? So used are
we to numbers for the purpose, that this sounds as
though I were asking, Can we count without
counting? — and yet we can.

Suppose you have a number of lollipops (you
don't know how many) and a crowd of clamoring
children (you don't know how many). You distrib-
ute the lollipops, one to a child, and when you are
finished, all the children have lollipops and you still
have additional lollipops in your hand. Obviously,
then, even without counting in the ordinary fashion,
you know there were more lollipops than children.
If, on the other hand, you ran out of lollipops while
some children still stood expectantly waiting, you
would know there were more children than lollipops.

But if, at the conclusion of the distribution, each
child had a lollipop, and there were no children left
unsatisfied and no lollipops left in your hand, then
you would know beyond the shadow of a doubt, and

without ever having counted in the usual fashion, that the number of children was equal to the number of lollipops.

This way of counting, then, which consists of lining up two series (one of children and one of lollipops; or one of all integers and one of even numbers) will tell you whether the two series are equal or unequal; and, if unequal, which is the larger.

Suppose we line up the series of all integers and all even numbers, then, as follows:

```
1   2   3   4   5   6   7   8   9   10  . . .
↑   ↑   ↑   ↑   ↑   ↑   ↑   ↑   ↑   ↑
↓   ↓   ↓   ↓   ↓   ↓   ↓   ↓   ↓   ↓
2   4   6   8   10  12  14  16  18  20  . . .
```

As you see there is an even number for every conceivable integer, and you can obtain the even number by simply doubling the integer. No matter how far you go, no integer need be omitted and no even number is missing. (Every child, in other words, is being satisfied with a lollipop.) At no point, no matter how far you go, will you find an integer for which you can't write an even number, and each integer (no matter how many you've gone through) has a different even number attached to it.

Does this mean that there are exactly as many even numbers as there are integers all together? Well, the phrase "as many" doesn't really have the

usual everyday meaning when we're talking about
things that are endless. Instead it is more proper to
say that the series of even numbers is "in one-to-one
correspondence" with the series of all integers;
meaning that the even numbers can be lined up
systematically with the integers so that there is one
of the first series for every one of the second and vice
versa.

You can also set up a series of numbers counting
by millions and compare it with the series of all
integers in the same way. For every integer there's
an even-million number obtained by multiplying
the integer by a million. For 1 there's 1000000, for
6 there's 6000000, for 2873 there's 2873000000 and so
on. So there are "as many" numbers counting by a
million as there are integers altogether. Or, at least,
the two series are in one-to-one correspondence.
Any series of numbers that is in one-to-one correspondence with the series of integers is said to be
"denumerable." And the set of integers is also
called "denumerable."

THE INFINITE IN A NUTSHELL

Of course, the "infinite" gives one a notion of
vastness and foreverness. It may even seem to you
to have no usefulness.

However, even if we concerned ourselves only
with small numbers, notions of "infinity" would

crop up. For instance, suppose, we were to divide

1 by $\dfrac{1}{10}$. Remembering the reciprocal rule, this

is the same as 1×10 and therefore $1 \div \dfrac{1}{10} = 10$.

Similarly, $1 \div \dfrac{1}{100} = 100$, and $1 \div \dfrac{1}{1000} = 1000$.

In fact, the smaller you make your divisor, the larger your quotient becomes.

Indeed, when you divide 1 (or any number) by a series of numbers that grow smaller and smaller, then the quotient grows larger and larger, and as the divisor grows endlessly small, the answer grows endlessly large.

However, what, you may wonder, is meant by "endlessly small"? Surely smallness has an end at zero. Ah, but smallness may be expressed in the

form of a fraction. Thus $\dfrac{1}{10}$ is a small number, $\dfrac{1}{100}$

is smaller, $\dfrac{1}{1000}$ is smaller still. There is no limit to

the smallness as you increase the number of zeros to

$\dfrac{1}{100000000000000000}$ . . . for no matter how far you

increase it you never quite reach zero.

We may therefore also say: When you divide 1 (or any number) by a series of numbers that grows larger and larger, then the quotient grows smaller and smaller, and as the divisor grows endlessly large, the answer grows endlessly small.

Note, however, that we can never divide any number by 0. This operation is excluded from mathematics. And for a very good reason. What number, for instance, would be the quotient if we tried to divide 6, say, by 0? We would have $\frac{6}{0} = ?$ In other words, what number *times* zero comes out 6? There is no such number, since every number times 0 is 0. So we can never divide any number by 0.

The interval between any two numbers, say between 1 and 2, can be divided into any number of fractions by breaking it up into millionths, or trillionths, and each trillionth into trillionths and so on. This can be done for any smaller interval, such as that between $\frac{1}{4}$ and $\frac{1}{2}$ or between 0.0000000 and 0.0000001.

And yet mathematicians have managed to show that all conceivable fractions (that is, all rational numbers) can be arranged in such a way that a one-to-one correspondence can be set up with the series of integers. For every integer there will be a fraction, and vice versa, with no integers left out and no fractions left out. The series of all possible fractions is therefore denumerable.

CLOSER AND CLOSER AND CLOSER . . .

Consider a series of fractions like this: $\frac{1}{2}$, $\frac{1}{4}$, $\frac{1}{8}$,

$\frac{1}{16}$, $\frac{1}{32}$, $\frac{1}{64}$, $\frac{1}{128}$, $\frac{1}{256}$, $\frac{1}{512}$, and so on endlessly.

Notice that each fraction is one-half the size of the preceding fraction, since the denominator doubles each time. (After all, if you take any of the fractions in the series, say $\frac{1}{128}$, and divide it by 2, that is the same as multiplying it by $\frac{1}{2}$, and $\frac{1}{128} \times \frac{1}{2} = \frac{1}{256}$, the denominator doubling.)

Although the fractions get continually smaller, the series can be considered endless because no matter how small the fractions get, it is always possible to multiply the denominator by 2 and get a still smaller fraction and the next in the series. Furthermore, the fractions never quite reach zero because the denominator can get larger endlessly and it is only if an end could be reached (which it can't) that the fraction could reach zero.

The question is, What is the sum of all those fractions? It might seem that the sum of an endless series of numbers must be endlessly large ("it stands to reason") but let's start adding, anyway.

First $\frac{1}{2}$ plus $\frac{1}{4}$ is $\frac{3}{4}$. Add $\frac{1}{8}$ and the sum is $\frac{7}{8}$; add

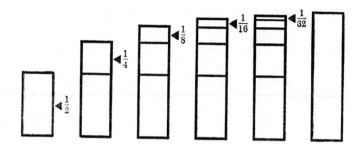

$\frac{1}{16}$ and the sum is $\frac{15}{16}$; and $\frac{1}{32}$ and the sum is $\frac{31}{32}$, and so on.

Notice that after the first two terms of the series are added, the sum is $\frac{3}{4}$ which is only $\frac{1}{4}$ short of 1. Addition of the third term gives a sum that is only $\frac{1}{8}$ short of 1. The next term gives a sum that is only $\frac{1}{16}$ short of 1, then $\frac{1}{32}$, $\frac{1}{64}$, and so on.

In other words, as you sum up more and more terms of that series of fractions, you get closer and closer to 1, as close as you want, to within a millionth of one, a trillionth of one, a trillionth of a trillionth of one. You get closer and closer and closer and closer to 1, but you *never quite reach 1.*

Mathematicians express this by saying that the sum of the endless series of fractions $\frac{1}{2}$, $\frac{1}{4}$, $\frac{1}{8}$ . . . "approaches 1 as a limit."

This is an example of a "converging series," that is, a series with an endless number of members but with a total sum that approaches an ordinary number (a "finite" number) as a limit.

The Greeks discovered such converging series but were so impressed with the endlessness of the terms of the series that they did not realize that the sum might not be endless. Consequently, a Greek named Zeno set up a number of problems called "paradoxes" which seemed to disprove things that were obviously true. He "disproved," for instance, that motion was possible. These paradoxes were famous for thousands of years, but all vanished as soon as the truth about converging series was realized.

Zeno's most famous paradox is called "Achilles and the Tortoise." Achilles was a Homeric hero renowned for his swiftness, and a tortoise is an animal renowned for its slowness. Nevertheless, Zeno set out to demonstrate that in a race in which the tortoise is given a head start, Achilles could never overtake the tortoise.

Suppose, for instance, that Achilles can run ten times as fast as the tortoise and that the tortoise is given a hundred-yard head start. In a few racing strides, Achilles wipes out that hundred-yard handicap, but in that time, the tortoise, traveling at one-tenth Achilles's speed (pretty darned fast for a tortoise), has moved on ten yards. Achilles next makes up that ten yards, but in that time the tortoise has moved one yard further. Achilles covers that one yard, and the tortoise has traveled an additional tenth of a yard. Achilles —

But you see how it is. Achilles keeps advancing, but so does the tortoise, and Achilles never catches up. Furthermore, since you could argue the same way, however small the tortoise's head start — one foot or one inch — Achilles could never make up any head start, however small. And this means that motion is impossible.

Of course, you know that Achilles *could* overtake the tortoise and motion *is* possible. Zeno's "proof" is therefore a paradox.

Now, then, what's wrong with Zeno's proof? Let's see. Suppose Achilles could run ten yards per second and the tortoise one yard per second. Achilles makes up the original hundred-yard head start in 10 seconds during which time the tortoise travels ten yards. Achilles makes up the ten yards in 1 second, during which time the tortoise travels one yard. Achilles makes up the one yard in 0.1 second during which time the tortoise travels a tenth of a yard.

In other words, the time taken for Achilles to cover each of the successive head starts of the turtle forms a series that looks like this: 10, 1, 0.1, 0.01, 0.001, 0.0001, 0.00001, and so on.

How much time does it take for Achilles to make up all the head starts? Since there are an endless number of terms in this Zeno series, Zeno assumed the total sum was infinite. He did not realize that some series of endless numbers of terms "converge" and have a finite sum.

For instance, the sum of the first two terms in the Zeno series above is 11; the sum of the first three is 11.1; of the first four, 11.11; of the first five, 11.111 and so on. As you see, if you add up all the endless series of terms, you get an endless decimal as the sum: 11.1111111111111111111 . . . and so on forever.

But if you work out the decimal equivalent of the number $11\frac{1}{9}$, you find that it also is the endlessly repeating decimal 11.1111111111111111111111 . . . and so on forever.

The sum of the Zeno series is therefore $11\frac{1}{9}$ seconds and that is the time in which Achilles will overtake and pass the tortoise even though he has to work his way through an endless series of continually smaller head starts that the tortoise maintains. He *will* overtake the tortoise after all; motion *is* possible, and we can all relax.

Series might approach endless decimals, which are not repeating, as a limiting sum. Such series can be made to express an irrational number and by

summing up more and more terms of such a series,
we could get closer and closer to the value of the
irrational number though, of course, we could never
reach it exactly. Such converging series are used
to determine irrational numbers such as logarithms,
for instance.

MORE THAN ENDLESS

But are all endless things endless in the same way?
Can one imagine an endless series of anything that
is not denumerable with the series of integers?

As a matter of fact, yes. Consider the kind of line
I have been discussing at several points in the book;
one with the numbers marked on it at equal intervals. Suppose the space between each number were
marked off into all the conceivable fractions. It
would seem that all the intervals between integers
would be fully and thickly filled up with thirds and
sevenths and millionths and trillionths.

Even so, there would be points on the line that
would have no fractions representing them, even
though there were an endless number of fractions
included. Remember the irrational numbers.

For instance, $\sqrt{2}$ has no point representing it on
the "fraction-line" because it cannot be expressed
as a fraction. Yet it exists on the line. Imagine a
square marked off with a side stretching from one
integer to the next (as in the figure). The diagonal

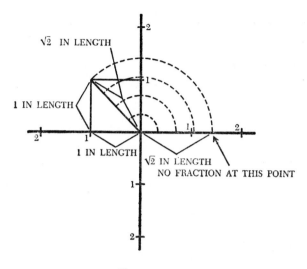

√2 IN LENGTH

1 IN LENGTH

1 IN LENGTH

√2 IN LENGTH

NO FRACTION AT THIS POINT

of the square is $\sqrt{2}$, and if that diagonal were measured off on the line from the zero point, it would end at a point corresponding to $\sqrt{2}$, and yet there would be no fraction at that point; there couldn't be. Every other irrational number could be marked off on the line at a point where no fraction happened to be.

What it amounts to is this: If points representing all the rational numbers are marked off on a line, there would still be points left over — an endless number of points left over, in fact. What's more, no two points representing rational numbers would adjoin one another, so to speak. Mathematicians have shown that between any two rational numbers, no matter how close they are in value, there must always exist at least one irrational number. (Also vice versa, by the way. Between any two irrational numbers, however close, there always exists at least one rational number.)

If, however, all the rational *and* irrational numbers are marked off as points on the line, then all the points are used up. The series of real numbers, therefore (which includes both rational and irrational numbers), forms a "continuum."

Well, what about all the real numbers? Are they denumerable with the series of integers as are all the rational numbers? Actually, they are not. It has been shown that no matter how you try to arrange the real numbers so that they can be matched up with integers one for one, an infinite number of real numbers must always be left out.

The endlessness of real numbers is signified by a symbol, C (for "continuum"). C is a kind of endlessness more advanced than denumerable endlessness, since not even the endless series of integers suffices to count the endless series of real numbers.

Other kinds of endless series can be checked for denumerability with the series of real numbers. For instance, the series of all complex numbers (which would represent all the points in a plane, rather than merely a line) or the series of all hypercomplex numbers (which would represent all the points in a solid — that is, in the entire universe, the universe being considered as endless in all directions for this purpose) are denumerable with the series of real numbers.

In 1896, the mathematician Georg Cantor evolved a theory of "transfinite numbers," according to which there are an endless number of different kinds of endlessnesses.

These endlessnesses he represented by the Hebrew letter "aleph" ($\aleph$), and the different endlessnesses were marked by "subscripts" (small numbers written under the line), thus:

$$\aleph_0, \aleph_1, \aleph_2, \aleph_3 \ldots$$

The first in the series is called "aleph-null" and it corresponds to the endlessness of the series of integers. This means that the vast endlessness with which I began this chapter may be the smallest endlessness that can possibly exist. No one, in other words, has ever discovered an endless series of anything which is not denumerable with the series of integers because some of the integers are left over.

It is thought that "aleph-one" ($\aleph_1$) represents C, the "infinity of the continuum," but this has not been proved yet. No one has found an endless series of things that lies between $\aleph_0$ and C, but no one has proved that such a thing is impossible, either.

The endlessness of the number of different curves

that can be drawn on a plane may be "aleph-two" ($\aleph_2$).

As for the alephs higher than aleph-two, no definite series have been found to correspond to them as yet.

Nevertheless, the concept remains of the endless varieties of endlessnesses beginning with ordinary "infinity" as the smallest possible variety of endlessness.

So the human mind which painstakingly began by working out the difference between 1 and 2 has raised itself to where it can fearlessly try to work out the difference between varieties of endlessnesses.

In a book dealing with the achievements of the human mind, then, one should not write THE END for there is no end. One should write only

INDEX

Abacus, 7 ff.
  decimals and, 81
  exponentials and, 134 ff.
  positional notation and, 20 ff.
Abundant number, 54
Addition, 10 ff., 23
  algebraic, 34
Aleph, 199
Amicable numbers, 54
Antilogarithm, 154 ff.
Arabic numbers, 17 ff.

Base, exponential, 106
Binary system, 142 ff.

C, 198
Cantor, Georg, 199
Characteristic, 159
Complex numbers, 173 ff.
Composite numbers, 52
Continuum, 198
Cube, 101, 104 ff.
Cube root, 115, 178

Decimal, 80 ff.
  repeating, 96, 128
Decimal point, 81, 88 ff., 151, 162
Deficient number, 54
Denumerable set, 188
Digit, 3
Division, 43 ff.
  fractions and, 64 ff.
  logarithms and, 159 ff.
Division sign, 43

Euclid, 54
Even number, 50
Exponent, 106
  fractional, 153 ff.
  negative, 110
Exponential number, 106, 133 ff.,
  146 ff.

Factor, 51 ff.
Factorial, 104
Figurate number, 101
Fourth root, 177

Fraction, 63 ff.
  decimal, 80 ff.
  denumerability of, 189 ff.
  exponential, 130, 153 ff.
  factoring of, 78
  improper, 68
  proper, 67
  ratios and, 120
  reciprocal, 76

Gematria, 19

Hypercomplex number, 181
Hypoteneuse, 121

i, 167 ff.
Imaginary number, 167 ff.
Improper fraction, 68
Infinite, 184
Integer, 63
Irrational number, 126
Isosceles right triangle, 123, 124

Logarithm, 154 ff.
Logarithmic scale, 161
Long division, 46

Mantissa, 158
Metric system, 85 ff.
Minus sign, 28
Multiplication, 39 ff.
  logarithms and, 157 ff.
Multiplication sign, 38

Negative number, 29 ff.
  multiplication and, 46 ff.
  square root of, 165 ff.
Number, abundant, 54
  amicable, 54
  Arabic, 17 ff.
  complex, 173 ff.
  composite, 52
  cubic, 101, 104 ff.
  deficient, 54
  even, 50
  exponential, 106, 110, 133 ff.,
    146 ff.
  factors of, 51
  figurate, 101
  hypercomplex, 181
  imaginary, 167 ff.
  irrational, 126
  negative, 29, 46 ff.

Number (*Continued*)
  odd, 51
  patterns of, 1
  pentagonal, 100
  perfect, 54
  positional notation and, 19 ff.
  positive, 28
  prime, 53
  real, 167 ff.
  Roman, 14 ff.
  seven-based, 138 ff.
  square, 100, 104 ff.
  symbols for, 18
  transfinite, 199 ff.
  triangular, 98
  twelve-based, 137 ff.
  two-based, 142 ff.
  whole, 63

Odd number, 51
One-to-one correspondence, 188

Pentagonal number, 100
Per cent, 93
Perfect number, 54
Plus sign, 28
Positional notation, 19 ff.
Positive number, 28 ff.
Prime number, 53
Proper fraction, 67
Pythagoras, 122
Pythagorean Theorem, 122 ff.

Radical sign, 115
Ratio, 120
Real number, 167 ff.
Reciprocal fraction, 76
Repeating decimal, 96, 128
Right triangle, 121 ff.
Roman number, 14 ff.
Root, 114 ff.

Series, 99
  sum of, 191 ff.
Seven-based number, 138 ff.
Slide rule, 162
Square, 100, 104 ff.
Square root, 115
Subtraction, 25 ff.

Theorem, Pythagorean, 122 ff.
Transfinite number, 199
Triangular number, 98
Twelve-based number, 137 ff
Two-based number, 142 ff.

Whole number, 63

Zeno, 193
Zero, 21
  exponential, 109
  multiplication by, 39